Kneel Said the Night

a hybrid book in half notes

Sundress Publications • Knoxville, TN

Editor: Saba Razvi
Editorial Assistants: Erin Elizabeth Smith, Kanika Lawton
Editorial Interns: Eden Stiger, Kaylee Young-Eun Jeong, Nicole Bethune Winters

Colophon: This book is set in Lora.
Cover Image: Margo Berdeshevsky
Cover Design: Kristen Ton
Book Design: Tennison S. Black

Kneel Said the Night

a hybrid book in half notes

Margo Berdeshevsky

Acknowledgements

Many thanks to these journals where sections of the book have been published and/or appeared in earlier versions:

& Now Anthology, "Square Black Key"
The American Journal of Poetry, "Ends of the Rain," and "Down To Sleep"
Aunt Flo Anthology, "On Cue"
Big Other, "Tattoo Tribal"
Collagist, "My Own, My White Plume," "A Winter's Verse," and "Down To Sleep"
Cutthroat, "Lower Than Angels"
Dark Matter: Women Witnessing, "Half Notes"
Dark Matter: Women Witnessing, Extinction Illness Issue "Stand"
Jacaar_One, "Stand"
Kenyon Review, "Square Black Key"
New Critique, "Caged"
Rusted Radishes, "Hunters"
Tupelo Quarterly, "Felicitas"

Contents

No *hour is ever eternity, but it has its right to weep.*
—Zora Neale Hurston

One

Half Notes

To be dead grows on one, sweetly. Not knowing what time it is.
—Alice Notley

Call these notes. Half notes. Grace notes. I can only speak with small, sharp breaths that hurt my lungs, small bursts of paragraphs and lines. Half notes for knowing. Call them the voices that are in me. In these ragged months of global ache, death is one of the many inevitable(s), closer than my heartbeat. We all know this, but I've had a personal mantra for years, *I am the woman who asks how close is death, how near is God.* The subject is not new to me. A haunting tune. I used to be afraid to come too close to an accident in the street, or a lover who was too much older than me. That changed. I attended disasters, touched hurt bodies. I began to think about healing. Touching. Honesty. I once admitted to an older lover, as we lay naked and pleasured, that I was afraid to catch his age. Fortunately, he was compassionate. I asked if he minded my question.

When I was younger I used to have a practice: before I went to sleep each night I would curl myself in and say, all right, this is the end of my life—this life—I'm dying now (a carryover from the *now I lay me down to sleep* prayer I used to whisper as a little girl). I'd say to myself: I'm dying now, and if I wake tomorrow, it will be another life, and I will see if I have learned anything from this one to carry forward. It was an exercise. I was trying to teach myself about reincarnation. Learning *something* is the only existential reason I've ever found. I did the same thing at the end of a marriage. Lay all night in the empty grass and said, over and over, when I rise, it will be the next life.

But our collective terrible illness has changed all I thought I believed. It hovers, angel or vulture, how can I know? I'm one of millions, daring to ask without answers.

＊

And the great unknowing sits on my shoulders, yours, without wings. In our solos. No honey in sight. Mice have found the seeds I scattered. Offered to blackbirds. Let them come to my window sill, I who cannot fly. Brave little wings, be my hum in the drone of morning. Again, as in another odd story, my left hand curls in like a bird's claw, nails becoming talons now, sharper than before. I don't know who I am becoming. And the great unknowing sits on my shoulders—yours—ours—without wings. Enlightenment is the acceptance of the unacceptable, my old friend said and said as he was dying and dying ... May we all shine brilliantly, I couldn't say.

One day, the devil's story in Paris is about prostitutes in woodlands of the Bois de Boulogne: young young young girls from the Eastern European borders brought when they were just old enough to menstruate, or not even. Now their Johns and their pimps have disappeared for fear of the great illness. Left them in tents hidden in the branches, girls still busy as hell opening their legs for men descending under cover of midnight. Some bring them bottles of whisky, the story says. Under the branches. Under the static of missing wings. And the coughing, infected girls are dying in the thickets one by one. A call on a nearly expired phone card to anyone, someone, to say goodbye. Someone hears the story. Is that all? Yes. No word if their Johns have died? No.

One blackbird returns to my sill to see how my claw is progressing. To cry that mice have stolen my offered gift. Yes, I nod through the closed glass. Yes. She lands on the nodding branch of last year's boxed geranium, dry now, but sturdy enough for her landing. Glint-winged, black winged, she's considering my eyes. Are they berries? Could she eat them? *If I were you*, she clicks her beak against the glass, compassionate, even so, *I'd learn today how to fly. It will be useful in time to come.* My heart stammers at her rhythm and I think I hear her sentences, even so. She shows me her claw. I show her mine. Angry at loss and dying and the devil's will that stalks our days. Is that who is near? Philosophy 101 will do us no good today. No honey in sight.

Unknowing weighs on our necks, on our shoulders. Can break our wings if we have any, break our hearts that beat together out of sync, stuttering with few syllables left. If we have voice, at least that, let us sound. We raise our sounds. Like fists. Through the skies. Through the glass I tell her about the girls in the Bois de Boulogne. Might she who can fly visit ones who still live and bring a morning air of comfort? No, she cries, *We are beyond that now. You read that story in* Le Monde, *didn't you?* We lower our heads. No, I say, in L'Observateur. She nods. *The world is observed,* she says. Yes, I say. Yes. *The world is observed. With and without wings.*

✳

Another fact of life and dying has insisted I pay attention. I have been outliving my lovers, husbands, friends, one by one by one. I can count them all. One died at the beginning of the Covid 19 lockdown. I still don't know exactly how. We were estranged. I learned of it on the internet. Someone thought I should know. I am neither young enough nor old enough to be immune. Neither was he. Wise women of the world, we whisper, drink whisky and honey, avoid kisses or caresses, you cannot know where the viral zoo hides its toy animals, or humans, or dolls.

But refugee children are still crying for any life and their mamas in America's cruelest camps like cages, aren't they? Maybe this is the sci fi film that will no longer end when the theatre lights come up. So how dare I complain? Dark star, I whisper in the frequency of solitudes, lift me. You look like you must be mourning's love, despite the next poem I have no heart to write ...

✳

I am the woman who asks how

close is a death, how near is a god.

I am the woman who

asks does order, or its shattered

window—shout? Asks what can

the scholar cry? Is there a scientist

in our house (for nothing left...)

Sparrow, eye on a god with no name

for us, what did you find?

✳

I used to visit with old women. I thought I needed to learn how to become one. I photographed their spotted hands, their see-through veins, their milk-stained wide eyes. I was very often a vagrant, a traveler needing to know how to age — and yes, how to die. I prayed when I knew how, and then I forgot how. I told myself I have two legs. My wings are not broken. I'd tell myself, Ok, blonde. Ok, sixty plus. Ok, an emotional centipede, a poet, a vagabond. Ok, she drinks tea with milk, café au lait, when it doesn't make her breasts ache. Ok, is homeless in spirit and had a house for a long time — between a sleeping volcano and the wind-slapped sea and nowhere — now she has a *pied à terre* in Paris. Lucky bitch. Scared. Suckles love like every other human flesh. Fat. Thin. Needless. Meditative. Scared.

Can sing in an alto-husk sort of a way. Can climb hills. Can speak French very well, Russian very badly, can say good night in Indonesian, good morning in Tagalog. Can dance a tango, barefoot, worries about her shape, waltzes clumsily. But a survivor. Likes nakedness, Renoir, early Picasso, late Pinter, late Shakespeare, early W.S. Merwin, nature, beauty, sex, cognac, museums, cello, empty space, solid oak tables, old torqued trees with twisted fattened trunks and dwarf red birds fighting over high notes. The taste of rain, the taste of sperm, the smell of Eau Sauvage Cologne for men splashed on her own skin, Fragonard perfume, the smell of darkest red, the smell of praise, bundled wheat, mountains, the cry that might be love, kissing, white silk, walking-boots. There are much wiser women. The tests of faith are like that fairy tale: spin flax into gold, empty thimblefuls of lakes into thirsty canyons. But I try, in the face of finality and endings.

✳

I don't know how to control my universe. I've tried magicians. They disappointed me. Controlled me. Rejected me. I've been lost, often. But I'm a woman who asks. I'm the woman who asks how close is death, how near is God. Soul in a see-through shift. I listen and listen for my own late birth-cry and nod to the hands of the dead and the dear. I am the woman who cannot remember her own father's face in his coffin, winters and winters gone—no matter how many times she tries; there is no face. I'm the woman who's walking. Even when she is in confinement. Even in the days of new lockdown, not knowing if or how long they must last.

✳

Then

Locust crisis poses a danger to millions, forecasters warn—
The Guardian/March 20, 2020

They say do not speak of it. Do not say that there are locusts.
Or that your walls are fever tight as a size 6 dress

when your breasts are growing into sassy women. Do not say you fear the sun, or hands.
Watch the blood geraniums. They may not enter your room because the window is afraid of

the rasp of pestilence. Its fire. That its vow will not bring spring, but rather hoods, blocked
breath, dead. Hold your black cat like a lover. He is not your lover. Your lover may not

enter. But bow to yesterday's ash because its grief was there to read. Bow to crows. Will
they dive into a highest nest to devour its infant starlings. Your neighbors watch, their

tongues darting like flies. How to save a bird-ling or a world? How to save a springtime?
Prisoned for our own sakes—we cry, we are not allowed to leave our rooms. One banal

visiting pigeon lands, climbs the not yet budded vine that scales our courtyard walls. A
pigeon. An observer. Not a savior. But it must be dawn. It must be this day's Equinox that

will balance daylight and night, this time—. It's promised. They say do not speak of it. Do
not jinx it. We will speak of it. Even of locusts. And there will be breath.

There will. We will.   Then.

Or

Ask, does order or its shattered

window—shout? Ask what can

the scholar cry? Is there a scientist

      in our house, for nothing left.

Because tidal waves emptied again

last night, because islands of the land of the rising

sun, spun to corpse pieces, house pieces,

      skin.

Because grandmothers who ran in village

lanes, burning, once before, aged

to what the day gorged, then sent back,

      newly washed.

Ready to burn again sons,

without children, lost,

but their radiant chimneys,

      blistering.

 Because on the same earth I hold the crow-

born dawn, hold swift-songed morning's fresh

milk, ask, if I cry, who can

      translate? Are there

alchemists in our house? I am

the woman who asks, after.

Sparrow, eye on a god with no name

      for us, what did you find?

✳

Raising her eyelids. Without eyes. Who are you, she whispers. Waiters at the local cafe know her and shake her hand. Am the woman who cannot remember a face in his coffin. She tries. She loves small animals, tall blonde grass. And the largest rocks. I am the woman who cannot remember his face in his casket, there is no face. I am the woman who wears black clothing and picks cat hairs from her sleeves. Who are you. I am the woman, stone in the winter, stone in the summer, a flower in her bed. She lights blood-colored candles. The woman who wears her best dress, early in the morning, no one watching. Am the woman who is beginning to — I am the woman who asks, how close is death, how near is God. There is an answer.

> *When she raises her eyelids, it's as if she were taking off*
> *all her clothes.*
> —Colette

✳

I am still eager, I said.

I have questions. I have more than questions.

Sometimes I speak a single psalm, a nod to my father's demand that I learn the Old Testament before he died. *For He shall give his angels charge over thee … to keep thee in all of thy ways.* I always want to know: How close … how near.

Everybody wanted a world that would remember, and heal. *But first you have to agree to do the soul's work.* An ex-priest told me that. *Do your soul's work.* What am I, then, allowed to forget?

I was scraping my knees on the edges of my aging and doing it well, and not doing it well. Scraping my knees on fame and doing nothing more about it, facing its own fears, when I met one woman, an old actress who said she'd been planning her last performance. For when the time came. Her husband wanted southern hymns, white flowers, she, a eulogy — to be admired, the actress, the mother, the wife, hostess, mentor, artist, healer, lover. Until she knew all she wanted was to learn a little humility before it was late, to come to an ending and not as a stranger, to wait in a garden and wait in a wilderness, needless, and to be listening.

As I become less, she said, something else can become more. I listened very carefully. A eulogy can be a graven image, she said, and I would like not to need one. But that would require humility, she said. What is that, I said. Do I even know? A thank you to who names all the sharp stones on my path to break my spiritual neck on. Thank you for the urge to find a self who can rest in the garden of humility and to know how hard I've curried favor all my days, need for recognition all my days, what I've been, as a talent and a woman. To find the aging woman lovely, result of all she's lived and smiled and softened and wept and needed and tried. Even now, when I have no idea if this is the end.

I heard the old actress once more speaking for something I know—or don't: *I will take you into the desert and there I will speak to you in the depths of your heart.* Hands open, without any more words, I remembered how often friends and strangers have told me, *love.* And that is all, and that is all.

✳

The streets were dark with something more than night
—Raymond Chandler

The first leaf of the death of summer had floated down my courtyard walls leaving its trail of vines to cling and wait. A pigeon had found her perch, witness to dawn as it lifted its shadows. Me in my white lace peignoir at the window, remembering yesterday afternoon's rendezvous. I'd been so in love with him, last year. Now he arrived when he decided and called to offer, if I agreed, sent texts from the metro to say *I was completely naked in front of your door but I got dressed to not upset the gardienne ... and what are you wearing?* So we'd ended. Grinned. Evolved. Surrendering to what is and what was murdered, last year when it ended but didn't quite, a simple not at all simple change of season while my heart cracked the way hearts do, at any age. I liked my lace peignoir. I had a French landlady many years ago who also counseled, *a woman needs to be watered like a plant in summer.* Yes. At the window, at dawn in white lace. I suppose. With a sense of so many endings. Which one to believe?

> *I live my life in growing orbits*
> *which move out over the things of the world.*
> *Perhaps I can never achieve the last,*
> *but that will be my attempt.*
> *I am circling around God, around the ancient tower,*
> *and I have been circling for a thousand years.*
> *And I still don't know if I am a falcon,*
> *or a storm, or a great song.*
> —Rainer Maria Rilke
> translated by Robert Bly

Two

Drum-Call the Hour

Was he your teacher?

No. One of my obsessions.

Stand

If ever I raised a daughter in this now—would I name her *time bomb* and wait? Char-lunged bird of no paradise left—Who holds the winning hand? Phoenix, have you any will left to rise In flames or in ice or in effigy —stand — This tumult of hands that reach through smoke keening — call it — salvage — scream — prayer   Stand. The black wind blows through me. Imagine the coils of organs inside a body do they want to be held by the skeleton around them when it burns? While it is alive? The forests are collapsing inside the body. Weight of scorch-stained air closing them in,   their bloods   drumming Who can they beg to hold them? How long will they still dare to breathe? Once in the flames, did martyrs have a moment of wanting yet, to live? One time I begged a lover to hold me, after — Does a tree, when she is wrapped in hands of fire beg to be held? Tumult of hunger we say world   Avalanche of hands   we say greed   Phoenix, have you any will now, still, to stand   ?

— for all lands burned, and burning —

30

Square Black Key

Let the snake wait under his weed ...
—William Carlos Williams

Once upon, the Norman coast woman, no longer in her middle American housecoat as she remembers it, now naked under fuchsia silk, recalls the old robe on its peg in once-upon Akron. Was it called a housecoat? Yes. A thing to knot and tie. *Oui.* While her country is going blind.

Skins like dropped petals scattered and buried between seas. That robe, quilted in shades of mid-summer golds, pearl buttons, red embroidered petals big as fingernails, June-bugs scattered on the collar curves, on the low hemline, on long cuffs.

Bore a scent of daily Nivea moisturizer cream, whispered femme, and craving, when she swayed inside it, down a flight from its pink banal and overheated winter after winter boudoir to the kitchen landing where coffee would need to be brewed, on time. Always on time. Often, she spilled it.

A menstrual-colored canary would be uncovered, and knew its job was to sing. A rolled morning paper would be given entry through the back door flap, to the accompaniment of a jingle bell. Now, none of that. One leftover word, on ice.

✳

Now, French silk, middle age, perfume bought across the channel at Harrod's, a second marriage content with its weight, bodies made for second helpings, artichokes, foie gras, a laryngitic cabaret song in the heart for the used skins, shed. Good to be a snake. Who needed old skin?

Awake in la Belle France, a white orchid flowering on morning's Tuesday sill. Object: a single Phalaenopsis petal. Object: an old robe. Object: sunlight bleeding through pastel curtains that did need washing. Another kitchen, another sill.

Back to the white orchid: will you live until one more fall, are you part of a whole story, or only soft as any woman's hidden petals, unsusceptible to rain or aging as other flesh? Ready to die? Ready not to? The wearer of the second incarnation robe mixes fresh cream with her aromatic Italian coffee.

What liquid, or skin, can have the flavor of *la vie, la vie, la vie*? She'll dance naked in her second kitchen this morning, right now. Take that, old robe. Take that, *la vie*. She's stripping jiggling, sobbing. Her eyes ache.

The white orchid that needs so little to flower, applauds. Drops a few pale petal peals, for show. Her husband does not come in to the kitchen to take away the pain. But wants his café crème. He's already seen her naked, anyway. But he hasn't ever seen her shedding her skin.

He didn't think of her as a snake. He does, now. Nothing but uncovered flesh left. No old once-golden robe that she remembered, here; no new life of silk, that's the thing—not the old, not the new not the middle, but flesh; no bastion against tedium or ruined timing or no timing, or black keys. No skin.

✳

La vie. And the square black key, inventing — surrenders to an arrival unexpected. Object: unanticipated. Object: unsentimental. Object: unwoven threads caught dangling at the window. Another thing: a naked, thirsty, hungry country crow lands on her sill and for show, he too pecks and nips and spits and sheds his feathers. Sheds his iridescent blue-black hues, his haunting voice dropping octaves, and more snake than bird, sheds his skin, too. *Ainsi-soit-il*. Defenseless woman. Defenseless bird.

Missing key: the un-invented savior.

Square black key, a thing no larger than a fingertip, points back at its timid hovering above-it digit, hoping to be pressed into service—the letter "I," impersonal as any other, but black, and white as a dream without color, story with an unborn point of view, body in its doorway, neither in or out.

Object. Key. One of twenty-six alpha-beticals plus symbols, numbers, arrows, ampersand, shift, the abbreviation for the word "control," a slash, a parenthesis, a dash, a tilde, all permitting eighty points of pressure not to mention the upper case alternatives and including the longer black space bar ... mute slave of the non-injured, for a morning missive in motion to a woman on La Manche, in coastal Normandy, probably still in her dressing gown. *Darling... how could you have known we would be so cruel?*

✳

Kneel Said the Night

I sell mirrors
in the city of the blind.
—Kabir

Kneel said the night, her full paunch moon mute as I am. Ask for words said the night instead. Instead, a turning autumn path where the shepherd and his dog lead their x marked flock, where morning's cry is a hundred made single bleat   made soon a thousand dry leafed whispers — made sunrise — to its lover, the breeze. The lambs and sheep are x'ed for killing. Hurry their soiled, white, woolen bodies as one toward sun. Slaughter ahead but not   yet. And my own marked tongue like a taut wound watch ticks trees, ticks bodies, ticks the veiled   and the beheaded, ticks presidents, ticks light. Ticks stain I cannot say or bend. Ticks last year's dead. Ticks this year's dead. This morning's mute as a moon killed. The lambs will be meat before any plea is answered. The reddening forest can hear. Urges syllables like breath to a fire. Can speak to leaf, lamb, path, moss, stone. — It can. Then I — . Land, I mouth — hill of the dead — as if a voice — I have heard of ancient bones unearthed mere roads away from   here. Skeleton of sounds,   poem, kneel   said the night. Kneel with me now with the slaughtered sheep, in case there may be any reply.

— in solidarity —

Until

Saint Pancras was beheaded for his faith at fourteen years young or   Your own faith
waits for summer's frail body to birth, or   You rise before light or sound because a train
before blackbirds or sun   The station waits for your — heart and knee — a metal mirror in
a mirror   Remember, your sister said, after the heart breaks, the body   or yes, you said
in the dim red hour   You lean on a silver cane for eloquence or   Forget, forget mute
bed-sheets, his untamed mouth   Remember and remember skin now   en route to   This
day's station-dark void cracked by speaker static to say *delay — your train will be late
following a fatality in car sixteen we apologize for the inconvenience*   — What was it to be a
life that died on a train en route to Paris between St Pancras and la Gare du Nord   Were
its wings unfolded?   War is en route again the speakers say — not in the station — in the
sunrise   What is it to live ahead of another body wings or not   as you fall —

✳

Jump, and you will find out how to unfold your wings as you fall.
—Ray Bradbury

New Old Wives' Tale
(or maybe—whatever became of Red Riding or the rest—)

The petals of the white ones draped like whispers, layer over layer, gauze-thin. Skins, veils, sculpted birds, but not birds. White irises. Witches.

Are the black irises the most rare?
Yes, that's right, the rarest. Lovely as wolves, eh?

Petronella was the old man's gardener. Muscled, freckled. Frizzed in all directions, morning sun bleeding right through it, her tawny hair haloed a large head. *And have you seen this one? She's the good witch, that's what I call her.* Petronella's Yorkshire accent boomed in the otherwise still garden, earthy as her thick bare legs. Her small scythe was working at the weeds, careful of every single petal.

I neared the blossom she pointed to, a double black, with a second flower of golden tattoos, an elegant erection in the center of it. I *ahhhhed.* I lowered, to breathe the most delicate perfume. I had thought it might be heavier, dark as the colors. But it was all light, levitated into scent.

To have tasted a little love in your life, but not enough. To have dreamt of a good wolf. But not the bad one. To have buried the grandmother, and the damaged past.

But I'd been feeling that revenant chill all morning. Covered it with deep breaths of country air. *Ah,* I repeated, already turned away. No time for bad memories. I was there with my notebook, to gather the names of the rare roses in the old man's garden, that was my project this morning. Though presences of some darker memoir neared, I turned my back on my own mood. Not now, I hoped. Not now.

They say Churchill raised roses to soften his "black dog days," days when he was doing badly, days when the destroyer deep inside him was raging or morose; well, so did the old man. He could rage, glower, and then raise roses. Could hire women to help him. Smile. Could bare his teeth. At them. Or at me.

I covered my own dark days with crisp linen sheets. Voile curtains. Extra cookies. Parisian wine. Parisian tears. Occasional trips to the old man's garden.

Here, every rose had its name and a tiny silver foil tag he'd engraved for it, and I'd always wanted a list of them, names like an orchestral tuning. Music, I thought, when you ran them all together. Let's have music. Let the buried psyche find some peace.

I'd visited each day that week, coming in behind the small planked garden door, like an old familiar. But I was afraid I couldn't remember all the names. Iron latch on a sky pale door, and inside, his collected Circes. The landscape had no pigs. It did have lambs, soon to be slaughtered and not knowing it. Bleating.

✳

I'm a country girl at heart. Basket of goodies. Gatherer of flowers. Gatherer of details—by intellect. A player—by taste. Not exactly Red Riding Hood any longer, by lack of innocence. I twitched my bare feet in the grass. Glad that the old man's Petronella hadn't run a mower this week of my expensive and well-worth-it visit to his house, during his trip-to-the-city absence. The old man was greedy. He charged me. But coming south was a birthday present to my middle age. A woman of sixty deserves gifts in the sun. And improved memories.

I'd climbed the incline from his ancient stone steps and wooden house, feeling old and determined as the landscape, myself. Left my shoes behind and walked to the blue garden door, ready to mull his twenty-seven varieties of roses and write down their names, this time. I felt lured as a sailor. Circe, I remembered. Hecate's daughter with the Sun, lured sailors to her island where she had them—and turned them into pigs. I returned my attention to his roses.

There was his gardener, Petronella, weeding silently in the sun. I liked her immediately. *Thanks for not running the mower this week, I love the silence. And I love your garden, well, his garden, but you do the work, right?* She preened like a mother pigeon, I noticed. I like to make people feel proud of themselves. The flowers she tended were watching us. I began scribbling their names, loved the sound the names made in my mouth as I whispered them all together.

Empereur de Maroc. Bishop Darling. Souvenir de Malmaison. Bon Silene. Comte de Chambord, Le Baron de Gobbard. La Reine Victoria. Madame Laroche Lambert. Mary Manners, Saint Cecilia et Souvenir de Saint Annes, Madame Gregoire de Saint Aechelin, Madame Hardy, Charles de Mills. I said them aloud and Petronella laughed. —Quite the party, eh? I looked squarely at her. Was she a girl who could play with magic?

—Let's invite them then. How about that?

She looked at me, animal to another animal. Her big head cocked to one side, frizzed mane drinking the heating sunshine, now.

∗

—How about just the men? I'll share, my dear. We can share! We shared an initial low-register women's laugh. She was a country girl and so was I.

—He won't be back until Sunday, I stated a fact we both knew. Then, —Do you happen to know how to summon spirits? Again we laughed, a purred music from our bellies. As naturally as flowers opening in flagrante. I raised my left thumb and let it bend all the way backwards, a double jointed twist, just as my grandmother used to show me hers. Grandmother, I mused for a quick second: *ah, grandma, what did you do with all the wolves?*

I touched my own breasts, just lightly, through my sweater, then I undid the buttons. Silence descended like a wide swathe, a black and pearled cloud. Distant bleats of the spring lambs muted. Improvisations between crows and finches lowered their volumes until we didn't notice. The crickets that come at nightfall came now, their droning lullaby that could quiet any other sounds. Petronella pulled off her work smock and let it drop in the grass. Her two dogs wandered off into the shade; heads down on their paws, they slid into dreams.

The gardener put her scythe away, opened her shorts, I put my notebook down, neither following, nor leading, we began to circle the garden, heel-toe, heel-toe—reached out our hands as we passed, as though to caress opened flowers, an index finger grazing pink-tongued buds. Especially the roses. The irises observed us, attendant; they were now skins and curling veils, sculpted birds, but not birds...

—We want just the men, I whispered. Petronella nodded. A soft growl was what she uttered as Bishop Darling turned into apparition and then flesh, and the sun again bleached through the cloud cover. We both knew that's who he was. Bishop. He watched us both, ghost to ghost, animal to animal. L'Empereur du Maroc appeared, flesh as well, now—standing like a pond clearing to show its largest red fish.

This might have been enough, we were only two—but Comte de Chambord, Bon Silene, then all of them, and the two of us. We inspected like jewelers, horse traders. —What big eyes you have.

One murmured, —All the better to see you with, my dear. We nodded knowingly, continued to inspect. Nails. Hair. Teeth. Shoes. Beards. Thumbs.

—I always check the thumbs, I said softly. She looked at me, ready for any crone's secret. —Indicates size, I taught her. Happy, giddy, silly, we picked. And then?

Our guests were experienced, we deemed. Le Baron de Gobbard plucked the black iris with a bow, and he brought it to me, humming. A tryst, I climbed him like the nearest oak, barely heard the girl say —Dear, dear Bishop Darling, while her dogs snored.

✳

It was time to let the dark dog of dark moods—rest.

To take off one's clothes, there ... petal by petal in spring sun, and naked, to say, —is a blackened purple iris with golden "tatouage" the most rare witch of morning in a secret garden behind its latched planks? or the wild white?

I left the garden latch open. And walked out naked, this year.

I'm a collector of details, but I told the old man none of these. He's content to have a rose garden. Let him. Content with his Yorkshire gardener; and a friend from Paris who says she's working on a collection of Circe stories; he knows my love of tales.

He sleeps all afternoon; and then again at sunset; dry pink skin flakes around his temples, into his eyes, peels across his swelling hands; he's becoming fat; and deaf; he's tired of being a laureate; he's had all the successes he needs; maybe he'll raise goldfish; or cruel black dogs; time for a new world he's said often. Let it die. Let it go blind. He means new ancestors. Kinder memories. Altered fairy tales. His age.

When he closes his swelling lids, in his old stone house in the valley of lambs and fogbanks, it's a simple past; the ones who whisper don't speak of me, I was just a visitor. He was my ... and then he became ... and

He used to be my husband.

✳

Three

One thing without stain, unspotted from the world in spite of doom mine own and that is ...
my white plume.
—Rostand

My Own ... My White Plume

—*Panache*, a French translator corrected me, the right translation is not plume, it's panache, for which there is no good translation. Yes, I know about *double entendres*. Mirrors. Lakes with no bottom, thin red threads of connection like underfed veins.

A new, woven shawl for springtime. I wear it as I walk to the Boulevard Saint Germain. There have been no bombs this week. This month. Paris is a safe place. This week. This month. For now.

A man who promised and promised and never showed up has been writing to me again.

Sends a Chinese proverb: The ancient Chinese legend of the red thread tells that when children are born, invisible red threads connect them to the ones whom they are fated to be with.

Over the years of their lives, they come closer and eventually find each other, overcoming the distance between, and cultural and social divides. Could I believe the seduction this time? Probably not. So walk and walk and walk. He's my dark muse. Let it go at that.

She thinks it began at a café opposite a museum. She remembers his long thighs, crossed, his scuffed oxfords, patterned socks. They both smoked. Smiled through stained teeth. He remembers the aisle of a theatre. "No Exit" was playing." He extended one leg and she tripped.

Edit the past. It began on a battlefield, each one's thumbs cutting off the air at the other's throat. A death in each other's hold. One of several beginnings. Another myth from the East ... Edit the present to a springtime moving of her limbs. Their skin more fitting for an older woman.

She's an older woman. The blush of the man remembering her, reigniting the never-quite-was. Imperfect. She buries it. Walking. He remembers the weight of her breasts under yellow silk, and that he should have   could have   didn't.

His swollen hands rest on his own knees. Finger an imaginary old Chinese proverb. Its red threads.

Editing. Their shadows leaning now over a pond. Swollen-bellied fish avoiding the shadows, hungry for sun-sparks. *We avoided the light*, she remembers. *I was afraid of your eagerness*, he remembers. Enter the editor. We were old souls, ready to murder one another again.

Instead we walked into forests, broken branches east and west, branches could be sculpted into knives. We hadn't the stomach for more blood. Exit the editor. We kissed from opposite sands of two weather-disturbed oceans. In between, old fish avoided trawlers, lines, and hooks.

—Last night in my dream, this time we lived together, he writes. —Old soul, you said, and pointed to where we, in repose, breathed in concert.

Again.

✳

At lunchtime women head for good or decent restaurants for different reasons, ways to partition the hours between chill and sun, hunger and wine, loneliness and solitude, art and mission, lassitude and a promise to move the flesh, to ignore the loosened muscles, the mirror of middle-aging with the memory of being a beauty, or not. They refuse to read the news. They—are their only news.

The café called Les Editeurs serves those who edit their manuscripts or lives or hours too. Some shudder like forests of branches, loaded with nervous blackbirds.

＊

There's a woman in a black and green belted coat, determined to be kind to strangers. Catches her reflection in windows. *me. me. me.* She's passed three stranded bodies curled over street grates on the way. No shelter, no lunch, soiled scripts.

Admit that the detritus frightens and angers her editor. She hates God, maker of desolations so piercing in the City of Light. Her Paris. Her darling Paris. She wants to kill God. Otherwise, she's a good person. Paris. Childhood dream, middle-aged refuge. Is her life common? Shared? Reflected? Useless?

Her kitchen table dances with a vase of blood-bright anemones, their black centers so like the center of her right eye, cut open for a cataract last week. Did it bleed? She didn't see if it did, they'd injected *Hypnovel's* heavy dose of forgetting to stop it all, the trembling of her limbs on the surgical slab while the nurse hummed under her breath—she remembers only that,

and then a dark center and a slow return to seeing the clarity of her century, her fear of guns, her body, shop window mirrors, men on street grates curled into detritus next to dog shit, wars in another city? no, her own, women, monopoly, solitaire, a disdain for the game, any game.

She sits on the banquette of the café, beside another woman couched in noon shadows. Women head for lunchtime for different reasons. She orders the same meal as her voisine, and they will exchange pleasantries. No. They will exchange dropped feathers.

—I cry every day. It's like knives attacking me, the banquette neighbor confesses, while I eat.

She wears a discreet round red rosette of the Légion d'honneur on her left lapel. Unasked, in a quarter hour, her life. French women don't speak this way to strangers. This one does.

Her highs and lows, her chateau owned, and lost, her lovers betrayed and betraying, her five children, her Chanel and Prada clothes, her fortunes lost, made, lost, chemo every month, the once long blonde hair —long and lovely as yours, Madame. Her autobiography written,

she's renowned, accepted for publication and lost —I lost my life again, the computer crashed, I rewrote it all better in three weeks, but I lost my life, I've been robbed, raped, betrayed, and yes I cry.

I cry every day. I'm a famous woman. Summers in Morocco or the Himalayas or the Vineyard. I created so many successes. And I cry.

—What do you most want, today, I ask. —A lover, she says, staring straight ahead.

—What do you want today, I ask once more. —Peace, she says. Peace.

—What do you do, Madame, she asks, sudden with awareness that I'm there also. Someone is listening to her. I am. She stares at me like a child at a new insect, into the dark center of my eye. She's awake.

—I'm not a famous poet, I say. Not famous at all. And yes I always want to meet a muse and a kind to me stranger on a bridge. Every day. It hasn't happened in a long time. My only lover is self. Solitude. Soul.

The editor is succeeding. The man who promised and promised...will not come to find me. The newly operated eye sees colors more brightly, now that its cataract has been sliced out. But the edges may remain uncertain.

—How old are you, she asks. I tell her. We are the same age, she says, one hand raking her scraps of new-grown white hair.

For a moment, she has paused in her mariner's tale of albatross and personal tears.

—There's a lake I went to once, I tell her. *Tamblingan*, it's called, in a faraway language. It was stiller than peace. It's up an Indonesian mountain past slopes of blue flowers, and then a lake as still as an unknown death of a pigeon at dawn. Stiller than peace. Ringed with tattered parasols, rain-rotted temple cloths, it waited.

—What does the name mean?

—*Remember the medicine.*

A fishermen's raft and a few boat hulls had floated. Decrepit temples at the periphery. A son of a priest took me there once. A bad boy who would not join the lineage. But he took me to the lake whose name means remember the medicine. He whispered like a screen covered with dozing flies, and then he left me alone and quiet at the gray dirt shore of that lake. And I wasn't ready. And then, so suddenly, I wept into that lake. I gave it all my tears for a very long hour.

—Who would you give your tears to, I ask her. She leans and kisses me, French style, on each cheek, and wraps her shawl of red threads and her dark coat and dons a wide brimmed hat to cover her scraps of hair.

—You are my muse today, a little light. She kisses me again. I remember the medicine.

Once, after I'd seen the end of the world, and I had, earth broken, houses torn, I remembered that place. —Take me there, please, I'd begged a stranger with inked jaguars drawn on every inch of his skin. He obliged.

The fog shawled us. Clustered and violent blue hydrangeas sloped road banks, then there was a path, and it led me again to that lake. —Now, go, he urged. Crossed his tattooed arms and sat blankly, a lost page in a field of weeds. He closed his eyes.

—Just go.

I knelt at the lake's lip and reached my fingers into it. In a minute I was howling. Everything forgotten, everything remembered, the lake received all I gave it. A thousand of mine, and then everyone else's griefs. The lake lay still, with its dozing medicine.

＊

The one with tattoos was waiting for me when I returned to him.

—They want you, he said more gently than before and I asked no question. Until my own skin was stained with his jaguars too.

Believe it, the hot breeze added, leaving only its after-chill on my skin.

—Stay, said the man, staining me one more time. —And now, go.

I don't know who said that. I, or the breeze, or the lake. In the matter of muses...there is no good translation.

> *The angel would like to stay, awaken the dead, and make whole what has been smashed.*
> —Walter Benjamin

Ends of the Rain

"... These things happen...the soul's bliss
and suffering are bound together
like the grasses...

The last, sweet exhalations
of timothy and vetch
go out with the song of the bird;
the ravaged field
grows wet with dew."
 —Jane Kenyon

Once upon a time, rains thrashed and pounded against windows, deafening as needles on corrugated tin, wild as branches tearing to ragged whips   —and then it stopped and there was black silence, no stars. And then, there were stars.

Silence, the word like a boulder, stayed. First, it was a good silence. And then it was not. There would be *No crying. No tickling. No giggling.*

Two small naked sons, fists like granite, were trying to be brave. *No crying.* A command. *Not a move. Not a single twitch.* They nodded.

Everything inside and outside went numb. Outside, even the thrush had given up. Shut her dry beak over a swallowed stone, would not sing of what she'd seen again, or what she would: the dim window, the small boys cornered, and a woman called "godmother," her staccato shadow. The blind, closing. The dark room with its promise. The thrush with a golden song could see, and was silent.

In a shut room, the boys lay back to back and squeezed their eyes into sealed boxes. Bodies, under a burlap throw, they loosened their small fists and touched each other's fingertips— just. This was their only assurance. If either one of them were to make a single solitary move, thunder would come. It would be shaped like their father, the bad god, and he would come, and they might be killed. Those were the rules they were given each time, and they knew them. It had happened before.

This time they would be very good.

It was the godmother who tied them. The fairy godmother their father had welcomed into their lives. *Call her "godmother,"* he demanded. And so they obeyed.

The godmother, glassy-eyed, tall, her chilled skin wrapped in a dark green kimono, stepped nearly on tippy-toes, delicate on spindle-thin shoes, ash trailing ash from a Marlboro between orange-bright lips ... while she pulled cords around the two small bodies. Closed the blind, and she stared at their eyes. They could not blink, they could not answer, they had better not cry. She stared at them until they shut down, both at the same instant, instinct of animals to avoid the aggressor's eyes. Wordless, they listened to the closet key, wordless, listened to the thud of a second door, and then the slick grey quiet came, it lasted and lasted.

Put away, only the thrum of their two small hearts remained. They weren't bad, they had repeated; but it did no good.

Outside, the stilled thrush had listened; she had no plan. Sharpened her claws on the bark. Sharpened her beak.

✳

This is your test, the bad god had told his sons. *Boys need tests. I won't return for any reason, unless* . . . They knew what unless meant. It had happened before.

The bad god was their daddy. The fairy woman, his newest bride. Bad and good were one and the same in a closed room with no sounds. But the bad god had the same blood as they had. Same fingers, same emerald eyes, same fair hair. His bride didn't. She was a fairy godmother who had not come to help.

They wouldn't thwart their father. They'd promised. The tickling and the giggling—which was how they used to make the terrible long hours mute into fog and pass, were gone. Just a tiny move. Just a way to get through it. A fingertip of touch. For unity, for belonging to someone.

But — No.

The bad god had seen everything; he could see, and he said No, *that's not permitted either, you know better.* Said, *Don't you know how to be good?* They blinked like puppets.

Tests. *Don't you know how boys are supposed to grow strong, and good?* They nodded, sunflowers about to break on their stems, after a drought. And they had been hurled to the terrible place again, where they couldn't save each other, so better not think about it. *Better not try.* Better wait for the good god, who might come. Or a guy in a good-guy mask.

They'd know if he did, by the marching, by incense smoke like a thin stream, pungent as it snaked under the locked door and into their lungs. They'd know because he might begin singing, or he might even begin to pray. Snake in, coat them in the dark and corded place and they'd blink to alertness. Then yes, they might hear him humming, yes, a melody they had all once . . . just once . . . and then they might see the barest outline of his wide brimmed hat.

Kindness. There could be kindness, if he came, they might be pulled out again. Soiled, speechless, but punished for long enough.

Saved.

Daddy.

Liar.

If he didn't come, and he might not, their two small hearts kept thrumming back to back against each other. Little boys bound and closeted for long enough, as usual. Their father was always the god. And they never knew which one would come. Good-guy mask or bad.

The godmother opened her front door. A breeze. On a high branch, just outside the dim rooms, the thrush unfurled her wings, then refolded them, opened them once again, for lifting. Her flight had a single destination, and a single return. With the vengeance of the wronged, she went for the godmother's eyes.

✳

The brothers wakened. Bare skin against skin. A Monday. Birdsong, silenced forever, was suddenly—there —just out there— it had begun again so suddenly. Patiently etched on its thinned and ragged branch outside, its voice opened now like a full sky, the brothers listened to it and to nothing else. It knew everything, and had it done the impossible?

✳

The bad god was painted head to toe in his own blood. He'd done *battle* for them, this time. That's what he announced. That woman who hurt them, "godmother," was *blinded and banished*, he said.

The good god apologized to them. *It will never happen again, that's a promise.* Their daddy would be good. They had to believe him. They were his sons. Taught how to be boys. And strong.

The thrush was stabbing with her whetted beak, just behind the shut blind. As though she could break in and make a grander difference. Her lovely song like a loving eye.

Now, their daddy washed them. His huge flat hands circled them. Stroked. Slowly scrubbed them. Added warmer water to their tub. Let it run so gently, smoothly across their thin spines. Scrubbed slower, large, then smaller and smaller circles. Leaned deeper into the water. Touched them each, and both. Slower strokes. Faster. Slower. Faster. And then without control.

They all closed their eyes. And they hummed a marching song all together. Later, dried, covered, combed, warmed, he allowed them, just for this once, each, to try on one of his wide hats.

This time would be *the last*, he said. And that woman was *never returning*, he said. She was *no godmother, after all*. He'd *made a mistake*, he said. *Big men admit their mistakes. Do you understand?* he asked them. They nodded, like toys with a metal coiled spring. It was a promise he said he would keep. She would *never live in their house again*. It would *never happen again*. The time of assassins and thugs was all over.

And so the bad god was gone, too. And their father was good. Only in their dreams, the boys wanted to fight someone, hit someone badly. That would not be permitted, because there was only one another.

The thrush resumed her song, like rains after a long pause.

✳

In a town such as theirs, people asked as few questions as the animals or the birds. The grown-up brothers never spoke of that time—before. They had made it another rule. It would never happen again. And they believed their father.

One man survived better than the other. One had grown to be a slow and seething male whose gaze and curses were mute. He frightened the neighbors. The other one seemed to be waiting all the time. Would lean against a tree, a wall, in a doorframe, tapping his fingertips together. Nothing more.

Those emerald-eyed brothers, people thought; and then they turned away to sweep their own front porches, to pull their weeds, to kill another vermin before it had babies in the wet seasons.

The good daddy who had saved them continued to wear his wide hats; he hummed more and more often, and more off-key, the pitch rising as he grew very old. When he died the brothers saw his spirit lift. They nodded.

Silently now, each brother put on one of their daddy's wide hats. At his funeral, the corpse thus honored, the brothers, not speaking, wept.

Outside, in an airless and unaccustomed heat, stars of the Pleiades moved down a midnight sky. Now the brothers stood outside their house where they had learned to bear with one another, and to turn away; their house where they had learned to look at their father and to say no more. To look away. Stood outside their kitchen step now, and spoke to all their ancestors in turn, and in that silence, were heard. As though stars were the bones of their departed ghosts. They didn't know from where...such a thought had come.

Even in the dark now, they heard the thrush, singing.

Their dead father's hats hung on hammered nails in the kitchen hall. Now their god who was good and their god who was bad had joined night and its million bones. They watched the sky like hunters, scanning for birds. Saw that spirit, how it had lifted out of him, and up. How it had moved toward the white-eyed stars.

They stood back to back, and they looked away. They could not leave one another, or stay. They could nor remember or forget. He had not been good at all. He had been their father and their torturer.

Unbidden as grief, a thunderous rain erased all the stars.

There were only the two of them, as there had been in the twisted and tied dark. As there had been in the warm tubs of water. And like a hurricane without warnings, they turned with their arms raised, and fist after fist, they beat one another into blood. Beat and beat and beat at what was left of one another. There was no one else to hurt under that rain.

Their father's funeral was holy. The box was closed. *He saved us*, one brother said at the very last to the other, who moved so slowly, and then at last, moved away.

❋

In a quiet street lodged miles apart from that town, now the patient brother stared at his screen; tapped his fingertips one against another, and waited. Such loneliness had no name. He hummed a marching song over his tea, fell asleep again beside the screen's grayed glow. Left a cigarette alive.

"Thug." He'd circled a word on a torn page of newsprint. Very interested in that short word. Very interested by violent men. Didn't remember much at all. Thought about his brother, then turned to his wall.

Good guy. The thought was allowed to go no further than the word "brother." Eliminated that thought; it burned a small dark room in his heart into char and dust. Left it closeted and eliminated.

The time of assassins and torturers and thugs was almost over. That's what most people wanted to believe. And godmothers were for fairy tales.

The brother stretched and returned to his screen and watched some uniformed men apologizing. Some soldiers. Some presidents. A king. Then he watched some men who'd been tortured. They unbuttoned their shirts to show purple scars. He switched the channels by remote. Some cars burning down to charred animal ribs. Some kind of a riot. Some weeping. Some men's words. He was sleepy. He dozed again. Left another smoke red and alive.

He began to have no reasons at all. Like the end of godmothers. Fathers. Bodies. Tied. Like the ends of the rain. No crying. Not a move. Not a single twitch. And then there were stars.

✳

Of Remembered Septembers

Not memory but the dust of memory—not dust but the dried ache river-ing as though it knows now where to flow, not the flow of hatreds, gathered, not theirs not ours but a hatred of not knowing still—in that sudden air   they jumped into to die outside fires not fires of peace or idea or saved memory but pieces of griefs in their hands, collected like other memory, spent, with the dust.

✳

Risk

Dusk hovered at the windows, winged creature that knew her name very well. It called and she raised one hand to let it know she knew it was there. No guard would save her. The bargain was fixed. It would slide into her room, after, and she would ask forgiveness later. But first, another man. The fixes didn't last long, or long enough. A quicksand of pleasure, what you want is a policeman, her animals warned. Yes, she knew that. Again. The newest man liked the heat of her fire, the friends with benefits scenario, take two.

Another one would fail to risk love, and she'd build the fire and say *yes, why not, come'on over*. She cursed and she dressed the way she knew he liked, dress in a full skirt, a blouse with easy buttons. *What are you wearing*, he'd text. *You'll have to wait*, she'd tease. Let the game begin again. Empty when he left, she wouldn't wash until the morning after. Didn't say don't return. *Don't cry*, he'd say, *I don't like it if you cry*. An object with no soul, after.

Don't show more than your armor tonight, she wouldn't say to any but her door. Okay, lingerie, but armor. Remember. Armor. Improving her skills, a woman who could have occasional bed-time like any man. Her misters-occasional were pesticides that kept nothing away but love. The animals gazed at her with the compassion only animals offered, whimpered around her body as she slid against the wall until she sat on her parquet like a child left behind on Christmas. She'd closed the door on a visit that was another strike against her tally. It was time to get up and make another fire. This one was for her. Just for her. She'd breathe in its flame and its goodness and dusk would have forgiven her and she would sleep the sleep of an elegant woman. Outside, lace lovelier than any lingerie she ever wore, a delicate new snow began. No winged ones, no more men, no more fixes until tomorrow. She struck a match and kissed the blaze.

✳

Fingers Touching What's Not Hungry With Ghost

When they told me her lung was a jaguar, an adder When she told me *I've had a good life I didn't sign up for being burned alive* When we touched warmed stones together When she said *let's walk the dawn into sand* No sunrise *I will tell you only once* *I hate this* And we kissed Heaven was the compassion of an unselfish shore I have known believers who know They'll meet their ghosts no longer Ghosts, a daddy in his fedora a mama Naked in her slippers and champagne Those who know the canoe leaves its cove With ash in its prow To be scattered to the waiting sea where Ash will join its woven garland Known those who know only They'll join for coffee at the same table The same sky in the grass the grass in the sky I know two, wed and badly parted, dead the same Morning on different islands and the friends Gathered each one to sail and to send their ashes Starboard from the ship they'd built together, once— Its name was *Star of Gladness* I'll ask for only sky *Now I lay me* and *when I die* It takes so little to make me happy After a jungle, after a rain, words— Burned behind me No pyre. Air. A tight dress My hands wide Open. Yours. Someone's. Touch me We are all the fields of martyrs and Heroines And friends. Give me your kiss forever Now.

✳

A Winter's Verse

Dark and sullen and mean, silken as a shut eyelash, suggestive of something under the covers at dawn, yet a bounding flyer on gazelle's limbs under a red half moon. She had had ... so much hope. The child was now her own. They could breathe in a kind of unison. She could hold each finger, and sing as softly as she'd once wanted to be sung to. The child would know her name. Know its own name. Have a few good dreams. Grow tall.

And he hated her. She'd fed him and washed him and sang to him, and begged him to love her, and received his egg-blue stare, a first week of cuddles, and then his purposeful scratches on her naked limbs at night, his alternating voices, a yowl and an out-hiss and once in a great while, the purr of male authority, in the mornings and in their last moments before sleep. A stare that had begun with curiosity but edged into shadow and then to a violence, torn. He wanted to hurt her. Both understood. She'd coveted her friend's child, and thought if only—well, she used to love all children until hers turned into the devil child, and she had to give him back to the night.

She cried, grieved, and got older.

As a little child herself she'd never been a beauty. Small-boned, eager, brittle, "artistic," her mother had insisted, although her hands turned inward like tiny reddened bird limbs ending in something close to claws. An abortion that didn't work, her mother once confessed. But she was kept. And grew to be a woman who lived at a window on a second floor.

Small crows, the filthy city variety, hovered just beyond her ledge in the late afternoons when the light lowered. Hungry for discarded bread or souls.

She'd lived with no roots. She had a small whispery voice. She'd kept parakeets at first. Kept domesticated squirrels. Took in the orphaned boy-child, who quickly hated her. Who jumped and broke her hand painted vase, broke her Chinese plate, broke her favorite teacup, all with nasty swipes. At last, she gave him away. Wanted to leave him in a woodland park beyond the town.

To say *I'm sorry. You are cruel.* But she gave him to the proper agency as she knew she was obliged to do, and gave up. Turned silent. Turned away. Like one of her parakeets with clipped wings, she watched her window. Living alone, she hung a grease ball of congealed seeds from the iron railing and waited, hoping only for sparrows who'd come near to dive and land and feed.

And now at last she wanted to help something. Nurture something. A light snow came in silvered hints, ahead of dawn's ice. She grew old.

In a dream in the middle of last week she lay in her childhood bedroom, indigo and white patterned wallpaper of an intricate webbing of unopened rosebuds and vines, a thin gauze canopy draped over the bed her mother had chosen for her to grow up in. A mother's surrender to having a daughter she had not wanted. *A woman should enjoy her bed in the world,* she was told. *And hide well from monsters. Never let them come near your bed.* She hadn't been taught how to recognize one. As a grown woman, her lovers were very few. Two. One was from the east. One was from the west. And then eventually there were none.

Inside the dream she dreamt that she slept. And that a pearl-headed pin, an antique hatpin, lay close on the sheet to her curled hand which wasn't exactly a fist, but was not an open hand that could touch or catch, either. She slept, the pearled pin-head no brighter than the shrinking winter moon. Size of a fingertip, the pin lay quietly next to her hand. She didn't touch, felt no need to wonder why it was there, she slept, and in the dream a man entered her room and neared her canopied bed, a wide-girthed and unspeaking shadow of a man who slid something underneath her pillow and quickly and quietly he left. She didn't recognize him.

But she'd had other not dissimilar dreams since she was very small. The shadow man always approached her bedside, and in those nightmares she would try to scream and no sound would come. She would scream with no voice until she awoke and he was not there. In this one, it was the same. No voice. Now, it was the longest night of the year. The crows were quiet, they watched the December-silver sky and the graying contours of her street. And smaller fliers watched too. Awake or still sleeping, she was unsure, wrapped in her long dark blue robe, she moved in her dim room and she lit candles to scare away any shapes.

The child she'd given away had survived the imagined woods and the agency and its ensuing life, and the woman was often sure that he had become an habitual stalker on her street. She never saw him, but she was sure that he watched how long the dark would last, that he watched how well or how poorly she was doing, framed in her window on the second floor. Better than last week when she cried all night in her high-backed chair beside a glass without curtains. She was sure that he noted that, too.

Better than the weeks before. Solitudes she'd never learned to welcome, intimacies missed like her animals, surely the ones she'd had must be dead by now and her bed was crowded only with her pillows. But she was better this week. She felt that her long season was ending.

The crows were soundless. *Remembering her mother, dead for forty winters, on the solstice,* they must be whispering. All their eyes were closed.

Now, lighting candle after candle in her room the woman hummed a snatch of lullaby she'd sung, before. And she stroked a long rutile-threaded stone that was lodged in her velvet robe pocket, a crystal gift delivered in another of her anxious dreams. The crystal was threaded with needles, thin and golden and reddened filaments inside it. A chill and smooth flat side and a more rugged unpolished one, it was exactly the size of her open hand, and shaped like a small scalpel, tip bent like the fine point of a flame.

In the most recent dream she'd known and not known the man who entered her room and left it, this time. Couldn't and wouldn't look at him. Stirred, stretched out her arms and then closed her own twisting small hands over her belly, a gesture she'd made since earliest childhood to calm her nerves. To seal the place where infants are cut. *Mama,* she thought.

And then erased that word.

Wanted, she thought. And then erased that word. Practiced a better thought. Better to become my own mother. *Father*, she thought. And wanted to erase him, also. Never the most beautiful pebble on the path, she curled around herself like an old tree's roots. Wrapped herself in her own arms. *I'll be better*, she promised herself, promised a very hungry thing inside herself, all night. Not until the shadow disappeared did she reach for the gift that he'd left.

Her hand grazed the smooth surface of the object's head first then explored its entirety. The tip was so sharp it could blind or pierce. In the dark of her sleep and dreaming, the shadow's quiet gift placed under her pillow, her fingers stroked it. Long. Pointed. This one's head was larger than the pearl one that remained still on the other side of her pillow, this one was the size of an infant's fist or a small glass doorknob. This one shone a little, laced on the inside with the fine network of rust and golden hairs. She balled her own hands into tighter fists.

She moved a word around and around on her tongue. A steady low voltage of electricity thrummed inside her hands. She held the gift, opened her fist, closed it, petted the thing as dawn moved at her window in ragged pinions of not exactly light and not wings, and she saw the object more clearly. It was not beautiful. It was cold. Another word came to her, and she held it under her tongue like a capsule.

Dreaming still, now she had two weapons with her in her bed. *I'm no killer*, she whispered and she thought that she yelled. *What is this for?* Bellowed it into the room, and out to the hallway beyond it where the shadow had walked out. Now she had a voice. Now she thought maybe it was her father whom she'd never loved, who answered her. *Love*, she whispered. *Protection*, she heard him say. *For protection*. And he was gone from her dream.

Finally awake, she touched her bare feet to a chill floor and edged along the far wall, avoiding the window that had no curtains. She tied her robe more tightly. Lit all her lamps and all her candles at once, pulled a heavy dictionary from her shelf to find the word she still tongued, left over from her dream. Her breath came faster. Her fingers found it.

Her hands were twisting again, one against the other. Her tongue was a busy, nearly independent thing inside her mouth. She bit on it until she tasted blood. Returned to the page in front of her. *Magical. For protection.*

Her heartbeat was a caged squirrel on its wheel. She opened her computer, tried to breathe slowly. Hummed. Nodded. Typed that word, and clicked the search. Lifted her hands away from the keys. Her fingers twined, as the substance of dream faded.

There, a precise duplicate of what she had dreamt filled the white screen. It was the size of an infant's fist, laced with rutile threads, and next to it. . . another one with threads still more delicate and more golden. And next to it, one that was sharper and ended in a point more like a small scabbard. And she touched the screen with just one finger from her left hand, her right hand turning in on itself, more bird claw than ever. She touched, and then the beautiful object lay completely in that hand.

Afraid to make the floor boards creak, she stood and then she knelt. Curled down into fetus. And uncurled. Still holding the object. Then she placed it on top of her pillow and left it there.

They're all dead, she said aloud. Now she hummed that high pitched prayer she'd learned in a kindergarten. Her feet twisted under her and she hummed the whole of the tune. She thought about the child she'd once given back. Thought about birds who were just outside, and their claws. Thought about the sharp thing she'd been given. Remembered pins she didn't want to use for weapons. Refused to. *I'm not a killer*, she said aloud. Remembered that word from the father in her dream, *protection*. And she spit out a long and very low stream of air when she whispered the words *thank you*. And then, one last time, the word that was a jagged pebble, underneath her tongue.

Yes, she was awake now. She decided she'd brew a strong black tea over a slow flame, and didn't open the door when the ringing began. Didn't open it when some voice called her name. It was the wrong name. Outside, nothing wanted to be awake. She felt no pain. But the child she'd once known had entered and would remain.

Four

On Cue

Was thin. Was an actress. Was it the year after Roe v. Wade, yes, two actors married a year, & ready to be Caesar & Cleopatra, not ready to be mommy & daddy, no skills for agonies of babies & discipline & griefs. That much they knew. She was scraped & they went on to court

Oscars, for suffering on cue. Was a year later the gynecologist pronounced her pregnant. Again. Lay thin & imperfect on the hospital stretcher awaiting cleansing that would return her body to her. He came to her side to say "all ready now, dear," & at that instant she bled, a gush that flowed all

over her starched white sheet, river of relief she was not pregnant he'd made a terrible mistake. In dim rooms where she lay other women to her left to her right, so many silent one humming, one crying she knew why or she didn't but she was an actress—there were other roles to play. Went on to cry on cue.

*

Home in an embrace & passion of sex again she stopped. Remembered being nine in a foreign hotel her mama jaundiced & flailing, a dying swan, a hepatitis devouring her liver, mama begging a nine year old girl keep her company in case she died. "Learn the combination of our luggage, baby. Don't cry. Never mind. Never mind. Read to me, baby," piss-yellow mama begging her, "Distract me, baby, read!"

Only book in that room is what mama's been reading all summer long, a doctor-story-fat-blue-covered-book named *Not As A Stranger.* "Read until I sleep, I can't concentrate when I read it baby, words are too small & my head's all trillium or lilacs ... will you just read for chrissakes, pleasssse? Help me, read, babe," & she did. Scene the girl reads out loud in her good-little-daughter voice, blond braids an unkempt crown on top of her head, wannabe actress, wannabe hunter, wannabe-saint voice is: an abortion with a wire coat hanger. "What *is* that mama?" No answer. The mother drifts, dozes, doesn't know.

The girl remains coldly sleepless seeing wires. Seeing blood clots. Seeing a sharp & low newborn moon hung in the hotel window, covered in its own blood. Hearing a high voice she doesn't understand. Awake. Mama is awake. "Baby! This is the combination of our suitcases: O - O - 1 - O - O - 5. You're a saint, baby. I want you to memorize that, *please.*" She tries. Loses a zero. Her hands are fists.

 "Try, damn you. Say it again." She says it wrong. "Again! You use it in case—if I die." But the mother drifts. Is sleeping again. "Babyyyyy." She hears her mama's whine. "Don't forget. please, my darling." And for awhile she sleeps.

✳

The actress cannot sleep. Or make love to her husband. Not that night, not for a long time. But she can always do—what her directors love about her, she can act. Can make it real. What makes her husband nervous and angry. What makes him whisper one night in the dark, if she does not have a baby she will never be a real woman. But she is an actress. And, she can cry on cue.

✳

A Day

I'm so small, I'm not tall but I can carry the world on my back. He was already bent forward facing flames, and he sang, boy-voice piping higher, his spine curving. *Dear God, child of God, have mercy on me, a sinner.* The one next to the bent boy mouthed those words known mostly to old men, old women, and monks. Flame ate the desert. It had already gorged on almost all the animals. A billion animals, the fire hissed. Or shapes of ash. The singing boy went from each to each, leaned a body against what was theirs, notes of his tune nestling against their syllables. They heard one another like bees inside a box. Comfort or grief, the heat insisted. If ever there was an hour for silence — it could be now. And one tree was standing still, twisting its charred branches, all its broken hands. Knowing its own song that none listened to, but it wore its necklace of moths. Moths are destined to live only a day, but there they were embracing her, still. *Darling,* they sang. *Darling.*

Down to Sleep ...

Tell this story on a Pentecost.
To hold a door open.
Tell this story when there are tongues of flame to be seen.

Daughter of lapsed Jews, she still didn't like their notions of a wrathful and vengeful God, preferred churches of any stripe, and ignored their hypocrisies. Liked their varied promises. The soft illusions of love as long as she could ignore their bureaucracies, and she could. Faith was a smorgasbord, she picked the slices she liked and avoided any of the rest. Wanted change. Didn't know how to open its doors.

A left-leaning teen, she had no preference for which ones, when it came to faiths, liked silence, incense, dim light from stuttering candles, respite from hot days, the idea of spiritual sex.

Once, in a temporary school run by gray nuns she managed to kneel for a Confirmation ceremony, white lace gloves and a coronet of white flowers, without ever being asked if she'd been baptized. No one asked. She liked all the costumes. The lace. The artificial flowers. The long gray veils and skirts.

She touched words, in the dark. Now I lay me down to sleep, I pray the Lord my soul to keep, if I should die before I wake . . . metal words etched into a black and white palm-size figurine that leaned on a shelf beside childhood pillows. She forgot it when she left that home and shouted Never coming back. No one answered and she no longer prayed before sleep or loved the parents she escaped. They saw their worlds from different mountaintops, and she was never coming down from hers.

Now, it was July, and she'd been on roads and no roads for some years. Slept on different couches and random stranger's beds, hippie years, post-hippie years, lost woman years. A believer in words she'd found knifed into a wall in a distant man's stairwell: Be not inhospitable to strangers lest they be angels in disguise. It was his copied motto and she loved it as a mystic's guidance in those days, that there could be surprises, promises, from the other side. Naïve as rabbits she had read about once, how before their slaughter they were so silent, how they met the hatchet and never made a sound.

All she met were strangers at first. And eventually the word friend earned multi-meanings. Friends might test fires with you. Might know what you were thinking. Or not. She had never been heart-smashed, just angry at what she'd left, just ravenous for a passionate life, she wandered more than a few years without evil. No believer in dogmas, she knelt once or twice, lit a few candles in random worship, random solace.

The bad thing was to be too alone, the good thing was to call some things love, never mind how much or how little. To chant for change. To write on walls. To be less afraid. Conversations weren't love, she knew that, neither were beds or sex, but if her heart was hooded, her spirit hadn't been sold out before the age of thirty. She was a free woman with big hips and a few lightweight ounces of trust.

When a nondescript church she'd hunched in for an hour that July night closed its heavy door at the nine o'clock bells, a stranger on its steps spoke to her in a tone rising and falling between jokes and a brother-like calm. They smoked. An hour later when the offer to sleep on his living room couch . . . his family was in the countryside for the weekend, and she'd left a traveler's knapsack a long walk or hitch from where they stood...she just looked back at him, his smudged Lennon-esque specs, his leaf-fall-flecked green eyes, and she agreed to the invitation. By then she knew he was a father and a town councilman and lived two streets away.

Plastic framed shots of his wife and two little gap-toothed boys laughed on the side table as she settled in on his guest couch, clothed, covered by a white quilt he gave her, and she curled and slowed to rest. Heard a clock's hum, and a night bird's chirrup. Her host closed his bedroom door, politely waving, *Good night, sleep well, wanderer,* and she slept soon and without dreams against his upholstered pillows.

Before first light she woke to the sudden weight-crush and brutality of a wordless rape, a tearing of skin and cloth—when he was done he spat a single sentence, You can go now, slammed the same bedroom door he'd shut so quietly hours earlier. She retched with no sound, grasped for her torn cottons and sandals and purse and fled too harmed to think, too numbed to howl. She ran for another place, any other place, remembered a desert town where she knew a man who was once kind, tied her clothes into better covering and hiding.

Walked. Grabbed a large black plastic trash bag on the street, emptied it and pulled and tied it over her soiled clothes for more cover and a semblance of shape. Mopped at wounds that were hidden. Hitched two rides in total silence. Walked more. Spoke not at all. One driver tried to talk, but then said nothing either, until they let her out in the light. Yes, she whispered, I've been to this place before. It was noon. It was hot.

It was a place where the town clock had a thermometer that read twenty degrees hotter than where she'd been. She noticed that, didn't notice how heavily her perspiration stank, or how it didn't stop wetting her, all that day. She was afraid to call the man she knew there. Not yet. Instead she took small and smaller steps and walked unseen and unseeing all that first day, and then a second.

Crouched, nodded, hid, stood, walked, couldn't erase the odor that clung to her skin. It didn't wash off in a middle-of-night town fountain where she tried. Unseen by any behind shut doors and curtains. Her scent offended her, she cupped her hands and poured the liquid over her head and clothes, animal at the trough, and no one passed, and no one saw. Dried under the brief night breeze, a late desert town was the only witness. She scraped at her skin with her nails, again and again and again.

By dawn, one clear thought. Some cash she had still in her purse could be enough to buy clean used clothes off the rack of a Salvation Army shop if she found one. It was the third day after. She waited in front for them to open, scurried inside, head down. Everything she chose was white. She begged for a restroom and threw everything she'd had near her skin into the bin. When she came out a woman at the register nodded to her now washed presence, and to her whispered Thanks. Maybe they'd sold to other women like her. Now she was hungry. Now she walked in uneven circles for one more day, silent as those rabbits she remembered still.

Desert day-heat hadn't climbed yet, her steps were vague, until she heard a low sound. It was singing. People were singing. Not so near but not so far away. Following like a child to an ice cream van's bell, the voices spilled from a small open door of a wooden building on a barren morning, a sea of Black faces there inside. She stopped in her all white clothes, sunlight behind her, a silhouette backlit by morning. The pews held a tide of shaded faces.

Down a single aisle in front was a pale blue wall painted with a mural of a John the Baptist, she thought. A Black John, pouring chutes of water over kneeling women, a circle of hands held up to their sky. A preacher's voice at the altar climbed above the singing and he'd seen her. Has anyone, anyone at all come here to be baptized this morning, anyone at all, you, child, you at the door, come right on in, step in, step in, and come on up here.

Motionless in his open door. He was speaking to her. Woman in white. He pulled and she entered like a giant marionette to an unseen rope, tiny steps coming to his open hands. Step in and come here to us. She obeyed. And in a minute she was surrounded by a dozen or more women whispering Welcome child, come to be baptized with us, and then, Speak in tongues, child, fire, child, speak with the spirit! They were touching and petting her, she was a beloved child, and they crooned. You came because today is your day, speak with us, girl, you're loved, and she was, they babbled sentences she'd never heard, no language she knew, voices spun to a sound that bathed her, familiar as a lullaby, and she let them cradle her and lower her head to the trough of water where she fell backward into their many arms.

Back to their voices and water and words, and in their arms she had no words for them but she let it be done. She cried in their waters. Wept. And she was baptized, washed, presented an hour after with a blue scripted certificate that said Reborn in the Pentecostal Church of Desert Waters and Morning. No coins could buy her heart.

She returned to a gravel road of the summer of her thirtieth year to heaven, not having read Dylan Thomas yet . . . My birthday began with the water / Birds and the birds of the winged trees flying my name . . . not having changed direction, only clothes and that wide stare of silences. And she walked.

Someone's lost sunglasses lay in the dirt. She put them on, they cut the glare, and she walked. Sun's rigid brightness was softer now. With the last cash in her purse she paid for a room for a night on a narrow street at the farthest edge of the town.

✳

At last she would dial the number of the man she thought she'd known there. No answer. An hour more and she called again. No answer. No answer. No answer. She folded all the white clothes and lay still and utterly naked on a clean sheet as night came in. Words she once knew stammered between her teeth. My soul to keep. If I should die before I wake... soul to take ...

No one new looked in her eyes all that summer.

Until the drying of all the leaves. Thousands of small red burned hands, or belated tongues, on fire. She wondered how one could count them all as they fell. Again in the dirt, a scribbled page lay stained, there. Readable. A poet's words...the loneliest job in the world is to be an accountant of the heart.

And then, scribbles of a note taker, maybe. These...the heron / Priested shore / The morning beckon / With water praying and call . . .

Another door, held open.

If these pages are ever found ... she has not awakened.
... Her soul to keep.

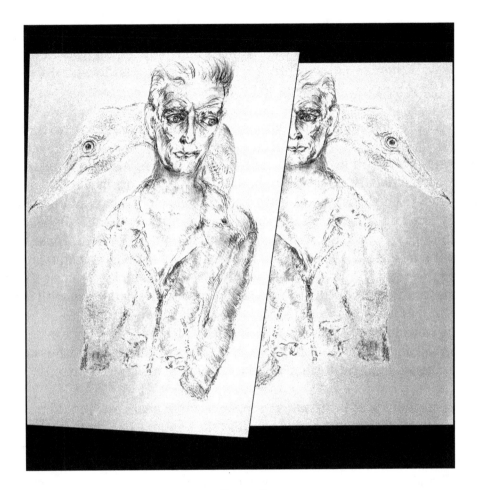

Caged

Billy's crouched at the top of the park slide, going library-paste white. Nasty yappy dog about to lunge. Kicking his heels on the metal, a bully overseeing the view from his up-there-perch. I want him to fall and break a bone at least. He doesn't. He perches there humming "O say can you see!" He wants to be President.

"Soldier, you wait...I could whisk you!" But he doesn't flinch and doesn't come down.

There's his street, down and over there, he can see it, where his best treasures are hidden under his bed on the twelfth floor at number 8, a block away from the playground. No one knows what treasures he has but he always brags he has plenty. I definitely suspect him. He has things that could hurt me. Billy's not more than four feet tall. Little Billy's called a creep by everyone in our class. It's the glasses. The scotch-taped nose. The smell. It's his whiny voice and how he spies in the toilet stalls and jumps out hissing or climbs up on the seat and looks over the top and hums at you. Hums through his nose, "America! America!" Or, always the damn anthem. It's the way he sucker-punches and gets away with it.

Boys especially hate him. I especially hate him. He nails me, and once when I can't take anymore, I break and they send me, not him, to the guard, and she says I have to understand because Billy's Daddy's been in the war. I should forgive him.

I didn't. I don't. Back in class I call him a creep, everyone hears me and then we all call him that. He shakes it off like a dog pissing on its tail. I should put that dog on a leash with spikes that dig in his neck. Instead, I get sent home. No one's home, I grab a pack from my own box of terrible treasures underneath my bed in my room on 95th street and head for the park, and there's Billy. No one in the playground but us.

I light one, and toss it under the slide. It sizzles and hisses and boom! black fumes slither up the slide to where Billy's still perched. Smoke, like snakes. Now he's scared. Can't shed me. Not kicking his heels anymore. Not grinning. Arms waving every which way and he looks like a wind-up machine. "Hey helicopter, let's see you fly," I yell at him as the smoke gets him and he's coughing and I'm all set to light another one when a guard shows up and twists my arms til' I let go and all the little red dyna-sticks spill out of my hands and pockets. Billy's slinking down now. I scared him. I know I did. I get hauled in and Billy gets off again. But I have a better plan. I need to get into his mind and tamper with the gears in there. I'm going to have to work on that as long as he's in this cage with me. Night/day/night/day....

We don't know the difference. Our same dreams are getting bad. He's in the top bunk and he's kicking his heels against the metal edge of the bunk again. Having a Daddy who was in the war is not an excuse!

✳

Tattoo Kin

Our mother had a tattoo. Burned on the inside of her womb, where I'd seen it, my eyes wide open when I was inside, before I was birthed. The man who planted me inside her had left it there, his parting gift drawn with the tip of his hard driving flesh. Later, I understood. That was their kind of sex.

He wasn't always around us, and at first I didn't know his name. But he visited. Brought me colors, crayons in the early days. His eyes like comic book dragons when he smiled my way, I touched him with just one fingertip, *hello/goodbye/hey*...afraid touching him might burn me.

Our mother never told me, but I told her what I knew, soon as I could speak. *Mama, it's inside you, there!* I pointed to her pale belly. She only nodded, petted my head as though I were just another animal in her living room; she had a dozen, cats, birds, mice, and me, all of us alive in our different sizes.

I had sisters once, I recall, but they'd left when I was born, she said. And then I came, needing her love. And that man said, *I am one of hers, girlie,* petting my head, too. Did he mean he belonged to her? Did he mean he was a brother? A savior? A father? A seed? No one told me.

The man who planted and who drew inside her—was visiting again, sitting like a conductor in our torn armchair by the setting-sun west window. Hands waving in time to a music he hummed more softly than voices of the mice, he watched us all the while. I knew who he was. Mister "Y."

I knew things, how our mother had been collecting our lives like treasures. She whispered that to me just once when I had a fever and she petted me all through a night. Today was

Sunday. All of us were present, even the sisters who'd left, and now returned, all gathered in the shadows.

Today, our mother was sick with her fever. Stronger drugs than usual, but she always swallowed drugs. I knew that, too. *I saw it,* I insisted, curled against her thigh, trying for just a little love, even now. *I saw it, mama, it's big as this,* I showed her with my hands spread open and apart, size of a small bird.

*And it looks like this…*I climbed up on our deep red sofa back behind her, an indigo blue crayon in my hand, and I began to draw on the wall above her head so she had to twist around to see what I was doing. She didn't stop me. She watched me. Her eyes all heavy from her drugs.

Watched my hands, my drawn creature spilling from them. She understood and she hissed in the direction of the man in our armchair, and he nodded like a huge puppet with no strings. I finished my drawing on the wall and the whole room nodded. My wild indigo lines made a baby dragon with another tiny baby dragon in her teeth.

That's what's inside you, mama. That's your tattoo. And that's our kin. You better admit it. My voice was a dare. The man in the armchair was still conducting. I was only the child but I was the one to tell it, sisters in the shadows and all the animals gathered, all kneeling around her, very still.

Who the hell told you this? Mama drawled, reaching for her ivory carved head of a tiger pipe. *The tattoo, mama, when I was inside you.* She hissed again at the man in the armchair, who crossed his long legs, uncrossed them, and crossed them again.

Now he began to sing, a deep-baritone lullaby, opening his shirt buttons one by one; and I saw what was hidden underneath, across his breast. Our mother was stripping her own clothes, stripping until she was fully-naked in front of us. Scratching at her skin, scratching from her breasts to her swelling belly.

Scratching to rip it open. No one stopped her. None of the shadows and none of the animals, and the man left his shirt wide open, staring at our mother. Singing. She was our naked mother. A picture crawled up to the surface of her mama skin.

Vein-blue lines darkening to just what I'd seen inside her when I was still there, and what I'd crayoned on our wall, what I told her I'd seen, just what I had seen. Her tattoo, bright on her nude skin, an exposed web of veins, a dark blue baby dragon with a baby dragon in its teeth.

Mother's heavy-lidded eyes hardened now, more like the man's. She stood all flesh and bare and she yanked the mirror off our wall, held it high, looked at herself for a long breath. Looked at herself and laughed. Crazy woman. I always knew she was, but she was my mother. Our mother. She spoke slowly. *That's us, my family. That's us. Now who's next?* And so I raised my hand.

✳

Five

Is it April?

She's hungry & none in her damned kingdom is worth kissing. Damp ski masks with holes for eyes. Monday, color of last night's used goblet left unwashed. Her *City of Light* isn't up to flamboyance. A winter princess has slept poorly. It wasn't the pea. It was—that she didn't love anyone. Was—that she was hungry. That any god or male she believed in was cruel, & withholding. None, worth kissing. She sent parakeets out in search. Striped cats; gazelles; leopards; dwarves. Nothing—She goes back to bed for the winter week. Loses weight. Curses. Night-mares that she's devoured by her pets who stride & stalk her realm, their now newly filled bellies, bulging. As though she'd never been born.

—For one hour, sun slides out leaving iridescence on her river, like vanilla icing. When night comes again it rains. Rains for nights & nights & days & nights until the river floods & spews, until its fish flail on sodden banks, each one morphing to a hungry man, & the men are of a single voice calling for a woman just like her. That's grand.

From the bowels of her own animals, shreds of her body weep as one. Those once-upon-fish, now men, hear a calling they recognize. It's this: *Be hunters!* And they obey. *Hunters!* They stride & stalk & slaughter leopards & parakeets & cats & gazelles. Good boys. Good men. Their hunt exhausted & done, all they've killed lie mute under an open white sky. Like dreams that end with pieces divided & restored, like winter colors finding new green, the desperate dreaming princess is back to her too-thick-for-a-pea mattress, her silken thick quilt, her size-eight body. Her city wakes flamboyant. Men. Women. High kicks & chocolate.

She licks her lips in new morning's breeze. All will know how to kiss. If not now, soon. All — will shed sadness' rags for promises. All—will sip wine from clean glasses this time, washed with a wakening princess' loud *hum-de-dum-ing*. Oh Love. Oh Love! She rises to Monday, *this* Monday, lone in her private bed. But: No canary, no striped cat, no gazelle, no pets left. Could she ever love a hunter? She never had. Never would. She was a pacifist. But she was feeling that today she might kiss — even a frog. & So she was humming. *Is it April?* she whispers, when he arrives. *Prove it!* While lavender hyacinths bloom.

& the frog is hungry.

✳

Hunters

She was a hunter. She came from so far away. There were quasi angels where she came from, some so old their bleached wings were broken. And churches, so old they smelled of used prayers. She wanted them. The prayers. The breaths of those who'd prayed them.

At first, there had been those times when islands seemed to her like newly drowned souls, submerged stones, only their faces sometimes piercing the waves and calling her into their oceans. *Come, and then let go. Embrace.* She could never capture them.

The settlement was nested below sloped mountain folds of moss-colored underworld velvet. The rest of the island was grayed with the steps of old death and almost no laughter. Patients sent there—never returned.

*

On the promontory called *Kalaupapa* was a jagged black rock pile located in cemetery B. She'd once been allowed on this island with the elders who massaged and touched its remaining lepers. The disease had a different name now, but they knew who they were. After a century of isolations, faces and hands twisted, fingers and feet stubbed or clawed, their eyes said *I'm a survivor, love me if you dare.* Her hands shook when she first touched them. A bone-dry landscape surrounded them, where spirits walked at dawn and at dusk. She wanted something they had, too. Something that had no name.

It was the season of mating for the barking wild deer who spotted the brush. Between overgrown palms and shedding ironwoods, people there nodded with each high-pitched yelp. These creatures would have offspring in a place where there were no children. A single buck stood large and protected by his does, his markings trembling over hard breaths. In the shadows, she watched his fear of being seen.

She was out walking again. Each time she passed cemetery B where a mass of the once-upon-lepers lay as nothing but quiet bones, a night-sea climbed in her. She turned to stare at the same pile of sharp black stones again. *I know nothing*, she wanted to say. *I'm here to massage the unfeeling limbs of the living, but I—* What she could touch were ankles swollen around scabs, fingers and feet re-formed as hooves with ingrown nails bitten by angry mouths. Beauty and ugliness had no mirrors, here. She removed her sandals and walked closer to the stones. Nerveless hands and old curses lived here.

I want to go home. She knew they'd wept on these dirt roads. Inside the stones, she believed a male voice was humming to her, as to a wife who once left him there, forbidden to return. *Aloha, my darling.* And a high surf broke in her for God's shape-shifters. A lighthouse beacon cast its long eye for the lost. And wind waited with the mating deer.

In a mute grove, she found that grotto where lovers had once upon held one another, in silences, or whispered goodbye as quietly as fingertips. Tree roots were gnarled as their bodies. *Aloha, my darling.*

Her own breath formed the same words. She'd said that, here. Now she fingered two small pebbles in her pocket, ocean-smoothed. Clicked them together, just to make one real sound.

... je t'aime ...

A spirit's touch against her cheek. That's all. With a short and broken hand. Her own hands burned. Hunters, underneath an inferno of stars.

One of the elders now stood beside her. But no one had been there, a moment before. *Come home*, he said, flatly.

If I could tear it out from between my breasts, home—I mean—I would—

Instead, she departed on the morning boat like all the other foreigners. She'd taken—stolen —only their story.

✳

And the next year, still a middle-aged hunter, she abandoned the statues and old churches of France once again, and she traveled to a different island. The farthest one she could find.

✳

Here, the decapitating and bruise-purple sea that had hurt them all, that had swallowed their babies and mothers and wives and hands, had paused. Was full-bellied. Had plenty of new lovers. And its fish were all fat and bloated and fed.

Come, darling, it's all over. Promise.

A tall and firm-footed girl had listened to the animals, returning. To the breeze, sweet as if nothing else had happened. One of the few left and alive, she'd outdistanced the water. And later, she'd made her way down past the broken dishes and mirrors and twisted columns and walls and pieces of pieces. She'd seen the shoes abandoned. The jasmine-scented prayers.

But she'd never seen—a woman who was this color. She wanted to smell her. Taste her. Steal her. Maybe kill her. Surely, she belonged to the ocean. Surely she was a servant of the fish.

The girl had skirted the edges of shadows cast by ruined things, and the sun returned with suffocating heat. When it was dark, she crawled inside the tent where the bleached body lay, its eyes still shut.

A woman—there. The girl fingered the dust where those sandals at the entry had walked.

Word had traveled quickly amongst the survivors. The stranger hadn't risen from her sheet and mosquito net inside that tent, not for two days, not for three, not for four. And the girl continued to hide in cracks and shades. To finger dust. To fear and to want.

And when her stranger was unceremoniously moved by the survivors—it was to offer her to the hungry sea.

One devil, conquered, they believed. In case there were more to come.

But the girl had a different idea from the rest. She climbed to the copper-colored roof of the only building that had survived the tidal wave. And there, shouting, she showed her truer color to the wasteful sky. Stole its colors. Wore them. Then she demanded bleached wings, and she pretended.

I could love again, she thought. I could be her.

＊

And for awhile...there were no more hunters. Once upon.

＊

Lower Than Angels

"You don't love anyone, Joan."

✳

Her mama's been in her suitcase like a swivel-neck doll in its toy-chest for forty years. *Joan-of-art-heart, Joan-of-art-heart, Joan-of-art-heart*, an un-saintly mantra licks her like a flame. She's a woman who—moves her lips, but can't finish. As though she were beginning to burn.

Ash sticks to her fingertips.
She's the girl who—

The girl is nine.

They're both in a twirling-heel and blossom-heavy Spanish jasmine night-heat. Nearby, there's the sea. A suspended flower is blooming in place of the stars, she could touch it, she could— but it's only Orion's ankle, anyway, she'd rather have God, and be a hunter, too. Her mama heads out dancing every night. Leaves her in a double wide bed. Kisses her first.

"Goodnight baby."
"Goodnight mama darling."

Leaves her to dream of woman-dancing, dark taffeta and swish-pretty, on a hotel terrace just below. They call each other darling. And baby. They're traveling women. A loopy wannabe dancer and her child. Tonight they're in Barcelona and her mama's dying. Of nothing.

She was fine, yesterday. Dying swan in the white hotel bed, dying of absolutely nothing, "Drama queen," her daughter hisses, a bothered swan herself. Now her mama's not out dancing; she's spread on the sheets; but she was healthy just yesterday, three-inch-heel black patent-leather feet, designer red-cotton-suited, ample padded retro-shoulders. Red lipped, spider thin on good muscled legs. Soft belly. *Mama.* Tonight she's in a silent wail on the starched Spanish sheets, arms flung open like exhausted wings. On an eighth floor with an iron balcony in a foreign country, her eye-whites have turned to a dark yellow, all her skin looks suddenly like old urine left on antique linen.

Her mama's sick and she should help, what should she do?

"Joan!"

Joan lifts a heavy black handle from its thin cradle and calls to wherever downstairs is, they don't understand her, she doesn't roll her *r*'s, she doesn't speak Catalan or any other language here, her mama's sick and the black handle doesn't understand her. "Doctor!" She drops the phone and it falls like shattering castanets. She shouldn't cry.

Horns claxon beneath their iron balcony, and long draped women, severe profiles with heavy breasts are carved into stone building fronts. Or else—are there ghosts there across the street. Suspended flowers are still blooming in place of stars. Now she cannot touch either.

"Never mind. Never mind. Read to me," her piss-yellow mama is begging her. "Distract me, baby. Read." There's only one book in the room, it's what she's been reading all summer long, a doctor story, a fat blue covered book called *Not as a Stranger.*

"I can't concentrate when I read it, baby, the words are too small, and my head's all trillium or lilacs... will you just read for chrissakes, please? It'll help me. Read, babe."

The scene the girl reads out loud in her good little daughter voice, blond braids piled in an unkempt crown on top of her head, wannabe-actress, wannabe-hunter, wannabe-saint voice, is about an abortion with a wire coat hanger.

"What *is* that mama?" No answer. The woman drifts, dozes, doesn't know. The girl remains coldly awake seeing wires. Seeing blood clots. Seeing the sharp and low new moon, covered in its own blood. Hearing voices she doesn't understand.

Awake. "Baby! This is the combination of our suitcases: O - O - 1 - O - O - 5. You're a saint, baby. I want you to memorize that, *please*."

She tries. Loses a zero. "Try, damn you. Say it again." She says it wrong. "Again! You use it in case if I die." But the mother drifts. She's sleeping again.

"Babyyyyy," She hears her mama's whine. "Don't forget. Please, my darling." And for awhile, she sleeps.

✳

Her mama's owl screams, running in her veins like broken chips of ice. Her own voice lowers like the ballerina Pavlova, her head, draped over her knees in a dying-swan curtsy. That's her voice. The miniature carved replica of the bowing dancer was always on the coffee table at home. Home? Her mother is always dying. Her voice is in her utterly missing home.

An artist has no home. She wants art. Voiceless, she wants ceilings with hovering wings, a thousand eyes in each. Other children want chocolate or dolls. She's the salt pouring out a needle-sized opening. But she's too much child. Waiting all night for her mother's death. She stands in the dark and sucks on her left thumb until the skin wrinkles. She hasn't done that in years.

She opens the double window, afraid to break it, stands out on the wrought iron hotel balcony, there are chilly voices that aren't hers, waiting at the hotel curtains, this is

Barcelona, and she counts men who pass under the street-lamp below, ones who are wearing black hats. She tires after counting twenty, twenty-two, twenty-four.

Hours pass and the scent of jasmine is too strong. She swallows a sour taste, counts the men who have mustaches, each one of them, the women who are fat, can't decide if they're pretty or fat. Then, her mama's awake. "Baby, will you get me water, please?"

The water faucet breaks in her small hand. "Don't cry baby. Don't cry."

She lives on and on until the early morning. And a doctor knocks at first light. Someone has understood at last.

But he really wants only one thing. "American Señora," he pumps the mother's limp night-gowned arm, "I help you, help you, of course! and you help me? When you go home, you send me this?" With a comedian's flourish he produces a golden and red cigar band like a rare diamond from his vest pocket. "Only American ones, yes? Yes, ok? I have all others from the world. Ohhhh, thank you Señora!" He's ecstatic.

Her mama rises slowly from her bed like a nearly-dead queen. In Spanish words that she never spoke before, that she's never heard her speak, and that she's never understood, her mama sends him and the cigars to hell. Everyone in the room understands.

He silently and grimly opens his satchel and gives her an injection, deeply puncturing her naked thigh. Her child watches the metal-bright needle piercing her.

By evening she is more focused. More the mother. Better than she was. That night she stumbles onto a train with her to travel to another country. To cross another border with her. Joan knows where the passports are hidden. Unsteady wannabe dancer and her daughter.

Just outside the train window there are filthy grey wings. No voices. She squeezes her eyes until they are unrecognizable. She holds her mama's hand. *She* is the mother. *She* finds the train compartment numbers. *She* turns out the bright lights. *She* opens the bunks and unfolds the packaged sheets. That night she has become not nine but ten. That night on that train the mother tells her, "Baby, he was a bad man, that doctor. Can you recognize a bad man, darling?"

"No," she admits. "That's a beginning," she says. And then she cries, but she cannot hear her, because she isn't there.

✻

"You're too sexy," she says to her, grimacing. She's been drinking. She's jealous.

"You're too much. You're a too-much sister."

She is—a tight woman standing in her mama's doorway now, trying not to watch her. Sees her hurting to be young again. And she—is looking at her daughter's low-cut black shirt.

"You'd make a good courtesan," she announces. "Inside, Joan, I'm just a girl like you."

In the mirror she does not know who she is.

"Go, she says again. "But darling, I love you."

Hearing the engines of wings that are grubby and soiled between worlds.

"Poor old Joan," she slurs, "your mother was a queen of Mulberry street. Now she's a drunk. Pity her." And then, "Honey, you could earn money with your looks. And you'll hate it when it happens to you, honey. Try not to get old." And then "Come'ere a minute." She wants to show a picture scotch-taped to her kitchen wall.

She's seen it before, her mama and a haunted-faced man with a thin mustache and a dotted bowtie, both perched on some wide Spanish stone steps, staring out.

"Silly me." A mumble. "I never told him I loved him. He tore his heart out like a bird caught flapping on barbed wire. Just like that. And I never told him. Damn me."

"We've been to Spain," a reminder in a whisper; she puts her arms around her teetering mama.

"Love, Joan." She slurs more. Wiggles her shoulders, then her hips.

Her child dances her toward her room, leads her to her bed, covers her with her favorite scarf.

"Never marry a man who doesn't send you love letters," she says as her girl leaves her pleating in on herself like an abandoned pink dressing gown.

She's wearing tight black clothes; her skin heats inside them, readying. It's Christmas eve and she's never been to a hotel room with any lover. "Mama, call downstairs if you need something, they love you." Scotch-tapes the neighbor's phone number to the bedside lamp. Her mama wiggles her fingers at her like a flirt.

✳

 She's a woman grown eager and not afraid. She'd make a good courtesan. Or a saint. For now she's a hunter. She likes men who have tattoos.

Joan of—. She's a sexy lover. A woman about to have a night-tryst with a golden-eyed leopard who kisses as if a jungle held her between its muscles. She does not love him but he's a catch. His skin, which is hidden now, is covered with inked heads, haunches, curled, crouched, leaping animals—all tattooed. She loves it. No one knows she makes love to such a man.

Leather-capped, long black leather coated, he's her personal Christmas-gift, he lifts her up like a dancer; Lincoln Center and its four shining theatres rise behind them. They've never been to a hotel together. His hidden skin is covered in a lace of permanent inks. He'll grin in the dark.

She's out on the New York streets being kissed, and they grow hard against each other as a Christmas eve snow starts to coat the cars. He's sleek and dark and fast. She unzips his pants between floors in the hotel elevator; his fingers slip inside her for quick touch, and then they walk out and to their room on the eighth floor, heads high and laughing,. She begins to sing. A little night bird, full voiced. Slow-dances toward orgasm, interrupted by the hotel telephone.

Their hotel room has double windows that watch over midtown Broadway below, each closed one Madeira-velvet curtain, and danced to her imitation-singing ... *Bayyyby* ... *Baby* ... It's a husky forties' song and her mama used to sing it for a lullaby.

In the leopard's arms, she slow dances toward orgasm, interrupted by the hotel telephone, and it's her downstairs neighbor to say "Your mama just died." It's Christmas eve. "She mixed her warm brandy and her blue tranquilizers, and she's dead this time."

It's too sudden-bright in the room. Joan slides the black silk slip back onto her interrupted nakedness, the leopard zips and buttons her up like a child, she stands very still to let him; and he'll take her home. Outside it's just past midnight and it's Christmas morning. His gleaming tattooed hand is taking her home to an empty house in the snow. "I hugged her this morning," she speaks into his thick coat. Numb to the snow. "It should have been God."

In the cab she's wishing that this were film, she the tragedienne who'd get the daughter statue. Swan. Hunter. Actress.

Through the snow, there are all these high cries falling. Or wings. Filthy wings. She thinks she sees a small one, beak open, perched on the leopard's right shoulder. Only one wing, and then it's gone. Soon, respectfully, carefully, so is he. She never sees him again.

❋

Won't enter her mother's room. Someone wants her to go into the closet, collect the jewels. "No," she mouths, ashen. "No. Feed them to her ghost."

And then it's winter, for years.

❋

One year, she's in Barcelona again. Because someone almost died here. "Mama," she repeats. "Yes, mama, yes, what do you want, now? Yes, I'm still alive. Yes, my world losing its eyes. Maybe I am too. Yes mama, yes, mama, life's an art. What do you want, now?"

She doesn't dance. She doesn't know what art is, still. She never became a saint or a courtesan. She's still a hunter of decorated men. It's Barcelona. She doesn't know where to go. She's learned nothing. She's afraid she'll begin to look like her mother. But she doesn't dance in taffeta. She stares. She's watching the sea, slightly blurred. The boats. Jasmine climbing a wall.

Reinventing this Spanish city: there was an iron balcony, yes, the bad smell of a cigar; the color of stained linen. She stalls. Tightens her legs. Drinks.

There's an old custom of *offering a libation to someone departed*. To a ghost. She touches her finger to her brandy, and puts a drop on the base of her glass. Drinking a warm brandy, like her mother. She dips a finger.

And she's noticing a male who's perched at a table open to a portside terrace. It's the way he's casually rolling up his sleeves to show off his arm muscles. Sleek. Decorated with leopards.

And he's flirting. He's eyeing a couple at another table. He's trying so hard to be seen by them. Wants the one with eyelashes that are long as bird feathers. But the couple is unavailable. He isn't going to get the object of his desire at all, she's watching, and she can tell. She's learned one thing: to notice.

They don't care what's sketched in indelible ink underneath his clothes. His flexed arms. His yearning. *We've all been there, my darling.* She's going to stop looking at him. And he ...

She tongues her brandy. It burns. She makes a damp circle on the table with the glass. *You don't do such men. Don't do anyone, now. Keep on eying the passersby parade. Humans—one, sparrows—zero. Men in hats, men with mustaches. Blurred.*

"Aren't you still looking for clean wings?" the man says very, very softly, standing right next to her table. "Yes? I think so."

The wings are no larger than summer fireflies this time. But they're clean. He continues to stand there saying nothing more. She wants to touch him, suddenly. Tilting her face with bravery. "Help me? ... I'm a woman who ..."

"tends to wings." He finishes her sentence.

"I don't want to be my mother," she says, unasked.

＊

He's finished her sentence. Circling slowly, for the second time around that Spanish port, daylight is losing its southern luster.

"Then be my friend," he says. "You, help me." What he wants is someone to share the scattering. There's a small round wooden box of ash, inside his satchel. Again, he says it. "You, help me." It's not a question but a statement.

At the farthest end of a dock where no boats are harbored, there's only the late hour floating toward a lack of color. He's asked her to be with him now, here, and she's followed to the edge of a long and unevenly slatted dock facing into water, into sky and less light. And facing his need. He opens his satchel, opens a small wooden container. One more time, "Help me. Because this was my mother."

There is so much ash from a body. He dips his fingers, gathers some into his hand. Waits for her to do the same. Wants her to participate in his ceremony. "Help me make it an art, Joan, please?"

Writing with it, ash unto air, they're children inventing an odd game. At the end it's hard to remove the vestige that powders their fingers.

Indelible as tattooed skin. Daughter. Son. Ash. O - O - 1 - O - O - 5. Lose a zero. Say it wrong. Redemption. Much lower than angels. Joan of art heart, now. Beginning to burn.

Felicitas

Downhill, there's a lullaby behind a low door. While rats make love in the garbage piles and a siren calls for an emergency or a miracle. In a room of erotic mosaics left from Pompeii's shards, there's an erect sculpted phallus. Etched below it, the word *felicitas*. Old Latin for *be happy*. And Vesuvius blesses the bay below.

It's your birthday. Would this be an all right place to die? You've heard there's a cemetery of skulls. You'll visit.

You sing in the dark. You take an afternoon train.

On a crowded train in a city where you were born, a man had pressed against your adolescent body and whispered *beauty, I will have you tonight...*You were very afraid while his body shuddered and you realized his sex was exposed and its seed had already spilled on your skirt.

On a train from Barcelona to Paris when you were a very little girl, your mother's eyes turned yellow. *Jaundice*, the conductor said, and you didn't know what it meant so you weren't afraid until she stopped singing. Her hair had been red, you hated the smell of her makeup and her hairspray and all the beauty parlors that she visited on Fridays. But you loved how she sang a lullaby that haunts you, these mornings. It's your birthday, so you thank her for giving birth to you. You whisper that, *Thank you*, staring through the train window. You've taken a train to Naples.

Outside, there are souls freed from hills, laundry freed from its dust.

You climb the hill to a cave where half-hidden birds flit, thin rock fissures let in some sky. And skulls and skulls rest on one another's long bones. Dead in plagues and poverties, a polished head, a child's hand-sized one, a tilted, tinier one, all woven together by dust, they stare. Outside, a high tenor vegetable seller passes. *Come out, come out and buy my garlic, my tomatoes ripened in our Napoli sun.*

You're in a cave at the retracted claws of a mountain. Twisting a question woven like a spider's home. Why aren't you in love? It's your birthday. You don't ask if love is possible, not anymore. Because there's no peace in your time, not its erect phallus, not its thick head of hair, not its polished open eyes. Outside, dogs fight, outside, slopes of husbands and mothers who twisted their hips until they birthed infants who cry. Outside, laundry, freed from its dust. Inside, reminders of what's under your dress, under your hands, under your hunger. A boy in a café with a different Jesus tattooed on each arm said, *Have you ever seen the cemetery of skulls? And you must see the veiled Christ, signora.* You thanked him and memorized the directions.

✳

On a train from Sorrento to Naples a man carries a box, in it is a polished and yellowed object stained by old soil, he found it while planting a new garden. He's tried to clean and shine it. He hasn't told his mother. He hasn't told his daughter. Not knowing what to do with it he's cleaned and cleaned and put it in a shoe box. He wants it to be far from his house now, and very quickly; and then he has a plan.

He brings it to the stacks and stacks of hollow craniums. Most, he knows, belonged to bodies that died in the plagues, the one in 1665, others from bombings in the war to end all wars. Does he need permission to leave his box? There's no guard, no gate. Does he need permission to stare? Altars to wives and husbands and infants and saints, all silent. Their only work is remembering. Before the sun sets that day, he has very quietly entered the cemetery of skulls in the city of Naples, and added the one he unearthed to the others there.

He's the only other person in the cave when you enter. Late light and shadow pour through its fissures. One dust-smeared glass box, child size, for her polished bones. *Cimetero delle fontanelle*, cemetery of skulls. A very modern Barbie doll someone has placed more recently, lies on top of the box. A red hair tie, a moist saint's face clouding into dank paper, a very long ago left grimed and plastic blue rose.

A single skull is perched near, polished and adopted. Adopted—a dirty memory card and a melted taper say so. A skeleton of a small animal lies beside it. Did the child adopt the cat or the other way around, both following into the cool shade of other skulls in the deeper caverns where the plague of their city had come to rest? You tell yourself the story. This is how it must have happened. You don't touch anything. But you stare and stare. You listen to what's not said.

... A girl-child who had always wanted a cat, begged for one, dreamt of one, its silk under her tiny fingertips, begged every morning only to hear the single word, No. Whose dictatorial father always said No. Whom she disobeyed. Was she that one ...

You tell yourself more.

Did both follow a one-winged bird or butterfly or bat, the single wing stopped last on a rusted grill? Something pretty on a hot day, its color of burned leaves, a child entering? How old was she then, did she follow a silked black cat into the mouth of the cave?

She wanted it more than anything in her life. Saw the shining black fur and followed it, a timid body and a scurrying one. A sun smeared day in a city dying of a sickness no one understood. A thunder falling of rocks inside a day with no rain, their sound heard downhill by those still alive, and uphill by those without eyes.

Trapped in there. Too many fallen rocks, none to hear her, none to find her after too many others to cry for, too many to bury, new caves opened behind the old. A loss of sunlight.

She'd followed the tiny, shining, black-furred animal into the cave where so many were already quiet. And then, there were years of quiet.

*

Inside, trills and singing of many wings, now. Bats and sparrows in a competition of sounds in the cave's recesses, now. Single drops of moisture failing to wake anyone. Candles lit once, layers of spilled wax now, and webbing between particles of very old prayers.

A single-winged orange butterfly grasps at a fence along the uphill slope. A boy pushes his cart, top heavy with mounds of garlic, their roots trailing. White dogs are barking at flies.

The man with the box has placed it beside the child-sized one.

He's staring at you. He runs one finger across his lips. *Bellissima*, he whispers. You turn to bone.

Downhill, song and polyester wash, and panties and bras and men's skinny trousers and wrinkled men swaggering no matter what time of day, light and the late wind watching. Nightgowns, loved or raped in the dark before they were hung in the southern sun and shade.

Downhill, a lullaby. And that room of erotic mosaics from Pompeii's shards. An erect sculpted phallus, its clay inscribed *felicitas*. Downhill, a church room holds a man who is prayed to. What is the sound of the swollen and static vein in the marble he's carved from? A marble veiled Christ's forehead, pulsing even though he's dead, a pulse like a dun sparrow's heartbeat before dawn light. The veil of the sculpted man is not inert. His death is in it.

Uphill, that sound of the *cimitero delle fontanelle* skulls and their webs and dust.

The living had cried and then prayed and then carried their dead uphill to get them away. Left them inside the open caverns high above the town. When flesh had dried, what was left were mounds of what didn't breathe. In later years, other dead were carried from a war-bombed port, up that same hill, left in the same open jawed caves and the flesh left only its skeletons in larger mounds. While newborn birds trilled just outside, and bats fanned their silences with black lace wing beats between rosaries and crosses of believers.

The man with the box comes nearer to you, then very near. *I would like to kiss you here,* he says. A voice no louder than the birds. *I would like to love you here. Please, please, don't say no. You would be so sorry, if you do not take one chance.* And your body is so cold. Your heartbeat is trapped like a wasp, between your ribs and webbed dust. An *is* and an *isn't* hover like the birds you can't see. It's your birthday. You don't run. You don't move. You allow a kiss. You have allowed a kiss. Against a damp earth wall. *I know you want to be loved.*

Your dress is stained. This has happened before. You make no movement at all. Satisfied, he touches his lip with one finger, then yours. And he leaves you there, motionless in the dim cave. Leaves you standing in the sound of birdsong and skulls.

Outside, a skittering cat. Inside, reminders of what is under your dress, under your palms, under your hunger. Lights stain the windows, one by one, when you finally emerge to the early evening. A dull colored wing leads you away.

The *is* and the *isn't* hover. You came for a middle-aged birthday. Were seduced. Frightened. *Yes,* you said. Didn't tell him that it was your birthday. Didn't die. He didn't kill you. He left you.

The air is soft as a cat's fur. And you are so much more frightened of being alive.

Superstars

Something with wings went crazy against my chest once.
There are two of us here. Touch me.
—Lisel Mueller

Later, the boy whispered he'd come there to ask her to marry him. She'd come to him formless as a sky's black ice, every night that week. Not her body. Her hands. His hands. Had done this before.

In the life when she had broken his hands. In the life when he merited her rage and when he fell. This once, he'd save her. He had a delicate leap-year ring, made of barbed wire clutched and cutting

into his own small-boy hand so that pearls of his blood made a bracelet around his wrist, and he wore his Batman costume, freshly washed.

✳

This once, we were nervy children who loved to dress up. Superstars. Watch. Girls who could do everything. Dukes up, dames. We said that.

Fire trucks screeched in and five movie-stud men —all selected from central casting—, five movie-stud men sped into savior mode, cranked their ladders toward a tenth floor window

ledge where my best friend perched on one good leg, the other already in limbo. A pale albatross with no more stories to tell, she'd told no one that one day, —once—
And we wouldn't have believed her. She's a baby of our century. She's our star. Our wild bitch who would grow up to have the last word. Everyone knew that. She laughed, wilder than any child

should, it matched the nearby park's raptors, a boulder released from a cliff, singing. She wouldn't. Nothing in her crooked body life could put her on a ledge.

Her eyes pierced my window from across our double-lane avenue. Her ear was tuned to the early dogwood in our neighborhood, color-dots exploding into blossoms. Directly underneath her one

firm leg, but just to the left of the clamoring metal ladder, the sweating savior's hand was nearly able —and the boy from our class who liked a joke more than anything else in his dress up day shouted *Jump.*

He had that twisted wire ring clasped in his waving hand. He shouted again, *Jump.* Gasps flared from passersby that met my owl screech hurled from my window to hers across the avenue's divide.

Our girlfriend windows faced one another —had faced — as we'd lifted pretend champagne goblets on each of our name days. Had pretended we could fly over the divide to say good morning,

and fuck you, and good night. And then the boy below her shouted one more time, and my friend who never missed a chance to have the last line sang *watch me leap* and did.

✳

Thank You

My deep thanks to Sundress Publications and its team for bringing this book to life; to Glass Lyre Press and Salmon Poetry for holding some of its earlier words that are mirrored herein; to ones who have inspired and whispered and read and blessed it along the night road, Diane Seuss, John Domini, Dante Micheaux, Robert Olen Butler, Judith Barcroft, Cyrus Cassells; to all the muses of morning and midnight, I do thank you.

Notes

I have a long and deeply held artistic belief that an author's published works may be, and often beautifully can be in conversation with one another, in the same way that paintings in a museum are able to speak to one another, across walls and from room to room. It is a way for an author's voice to grow and look backward and forward across her oeuvre in her lifetime as a writer. In that spirit, I occasionally quote myself, echo, or use small snips of older works in present works. There is a long literary history of such, Audre Lorde, June Jordan, Rimbaud to name a very few. In the book now in your keeping, I have mini-snips of poems or longer quotes used in brand new contexts. For instance in the "Half-Notes" opening gambit of this book, first born in my Glass Lyre Press book, "Before the Drought," and in my Salmon Poetry book, *It Is Still Beautiful to Hear the Heart Beat*, they live here in these pages.

Yes, she is a hybrid. The voice of this book is threaded by my photographic images, montages and sketches — a left brain/right brain weave of image and text, tone and space. The subtitle "half-notes" is an approach defining a process, a sometimes fractured, fragmented voice edging her way to a whole. Short bursts and longer narratives sounding note after note. Threading between a poetic styled prose and a highly imagistic one. "Half notes. Grace notes. I can only speak with small sharp breaths that hurt my lungs, small bursts of paragraphs and lines. Half notes for knowing. Call them the voices that are in me. In these ragged months of global ache, death is one of the many inevitable(s), closer than my heartbeat." Imagine a voice that enters, knows what it fears, stops, and starts, and stands again and again to offer — half in the dark of our/my time, half in the light. Each narrative enters the white space at the edge of the next.

✳

1 for "Half-Notes" (19): "ascent to light," photograph taken while climbing from inside a cave in Greece.

2 for "Drum Call the Hour" (29): collage of a found bird man and detail of a stone griffon, merged ... made in the cities of New York and Paris.

3 sketch of male as solo satyr by the author (36).

4 "one thing without stain" (45): montage of the smiling fallen angel head, replica of one on the portal of the Cathedral at Reims ... here, lost in a flock of pigeons in the grasses of France.

5 for "Ends of the Rain" (53): photo detail of a goat and Pan, found in a museum of ancient sculptures from Pompeii and Naples in Italy.

6 for "A Winter's Verse" (65): author's montage of masks and hands.

7 for "Down to Sleep" (78): a small Rodin sculpture of a crouching woman, photographed again and again by the author in the Musée du Louvre, and also at the Musée Rodin, both in Paris.

8 for "Caged" (85): "What Grows from Emptiness," author's double headed pencil drawing, overlaid.

9 for "Hunters" (95): pen and ink drawing of the multi selves in motion.

10 for "Lower than Angels" (100): one of author's many charcoal drawings of the dolmen stones in storms at Poulnabrone in Ireland.

11 for "Felicitas" (116): photograph of the piled skulls in the Fontanelle cemetery, (Cimitero della Fontanella) an ossuary, a burial cave, that overlooks Naples, Italy.

12 final image (119): a montage of mannequins seen through darkened windows in the alleys of Paris.

✳

The opening epigraph from Zora Neale Hurston, No *hour is ever eternity, but it has its right to weep* — speaks for this approach as the notes gather, yes, even to mourn, but each will make her sounds into the hours and the music of her time. My time. The single hour cannot be — eternity. But here is its gathering — for the book that is in your hands, now.

About the Author

Margo Berdeshevsky, born in New York City, often lives and writes in Paris. Her latest collection, *Before the Drought*, is from Glass Lyre Press and was a finalist for the National Poetry Series. *It is Still Beautiful to Hear the Heart Beat* is forthcoming from Salmon Poetry. Berdeshevsky is author as well of *Between Soul & Stone* and *But a Passage in Wilderness* (Sheep Meadow Press). Her book of illustrated stories, *Beautiful Soon Enough*, received the first Ronald Sukenick Innovative Fiction Award for FC2 (University of Alabama Press). She is also the recipient of the grand prize for the Thomas Merton Poetry of the Sacred Award, while other honors include the Robert H. Winner Award from the Poetry Society of America. Her work appears in *Poetry International*, *New Letters*, *The Night Heron Barks*, *Kenyon Review*, *Plume*, *Scoundrel Time*, *The Collagist*, *Tupelo Quarterly*, *Gulf Coast*, *Southern Humanities Review*, *Harbor Review*, *Pleiades*, *Prairie Schooner*, *The American Journal of Poetry*, *Jacar—One*, *Mānoa*, *Pirene's Fountain*, *Big Other*, and *Dark Matter: Women Witnessing*, among many others. In Europe and the UK, her works have been seen in *The Poetry Review*, *PN Review*, *The Wolf*, *Europe*, *Siècle 21*, *Confluences Poétiques*, *Recours au Poème*, *Levure Littéraire*, and *Under the Radar*. Her "Letters from Paris" have appeared for many years in Poetry International online. She may be found reading from her books in London, Paris, New York City, Los Angeles, Honolulu, at literary festivals, and/or somewhere new in the world. For more information, kindly see margoberdeshevsky.com.

Other Sundress Titles

In Stories We Thunder
V. Ruiz
$12.99

What Nothing
Anna Meister
$12.99

the Colored page
Matthew E. Henry
$12.99

To Everything There Is
Donna Vorreyer
$12.99

Slack Tongue City
Mackenzie Berry
$12.99

Hood Criatura
féi hernandez
$12.99

Year of the Unicorn Kidz
jason b. crawford
$12.99

Sweetbitter
Stacey Balkun
$12.99

Mouths of Garden
Barbara Fant
$12.99

I Am Here to Make Friends
Robert Long Foreman
$14.99

Something Dark to Shine In
Inès Pujos
$12.99

nightsong
Ever Jones
$12.99

Slaughter the One Bird
Kimberly Ann Priest
$12.99

Maps of Injury
Chera Hammons
$12.99

CPSIA information can be obtained
at www.ICGtesting.com
Printed in the USA
JSHW050953261222
35337JS00002B/49

9 781951 979423